Herbert Richardson

Paul Masterson

Fitzhenry & Whiteside

Contents

© 1992 Fitzhenry & Whiteside Limited
    91 Granton Drive
    Richmond Hill, Ontario L4B 2N5

The Canadians: A continuing series
General Editor: Robert Read
Designer: McCalla Design Associates
Editor: Frank English
Typesetting: Jay Tee Graphics Ltd.
Printing and binding: Hignell Printing Ltd., Winnipeg

The Author

A Professional Forester and Communicator, Paul Masterson (BScF, RPF, APR) has spent 45 years in the forest conservation, management, and education field, primarily in the Canadian forest industry and forestry associations. In recent years he directed the operation of the MTRCA's Kortright Centre for Conservation, one of Canada's leading centres for conservation education.

Canadian Cataloguing in Publication Data

Masterson, Paul, 1923-
  Herbert Richardson

Includes bibliographical references and index.
ISBN 0-88902-339-5

1. Richardson, Herbert. 2. Foresters – Canada –
Biography. 3. Conservationists – Canada – Biography.
I. Title.

SD129.R52M38 1992   634.9′092   C92-094013-7

The Inexhaustible Chapter 1
Resource

It was December 17, 1763, the year that New France formally passed to British rule under the Treaty of Paris. In his office the colony's new administrator, General Murray, was musing over a directive he had just received from London referring to the magnificent timber stands in the new colony far from the striking power of its European enemies. He was to establish a Crown reservation of suitable forest lands for,

". . . the growth and production of naval timbers . . . ."

This seemingly far-sighted policy for its time appeared to be the first inclination of a conservation policy by the new English colony relative to its forest resource. Actually, in the 1670s Jean Talon, the astute French intendant, issued a conservation law protecting the oak and elm of New France for use by the French navy. However, the new British policy came about because of the change in sovereignty from France to England. It gave to Canada's export the privileges of the British market which for the previous ten years had been benefiting the New England trade market.

Lush 18th century Ontario forest greeted early settlers

Canada's population then was made up of 65 000 French and 5000 British. This policy was not followed, because Canada had neither the resources nor the people to take advantage of it. For the next hundred years the prime motivation applied to Canada's forests and the other natural resources under their verdant canopy was one of exploitation.

Conservation, in word and fact, was a concept that was almost unheard of in the first half of the 1800s. The picture then of our natural resources and their apparent limitless horizon was seen as "inexhaustible", whether we were describing the potential of agricultural land, timber resources, fish and wildlife, water, or minerals. Robed in the mantle of exploitation worn by too many, our forefathers took advantage of the economic resources of a third world country.

Here's how E. C. Drury, former premier of Ontario (1919-23), in a 1939 speech described the situation:

"The prevailing attitude and behaviour was that of an exploiter and less of a developer. We exploited the aborigines by cheating them in trade, debauching them with whisky, infecting them with our diseases, and cooped them up on reservations as wards of a paternalistic state. We slaughtered the beaver in the woods, the buffalo on the plains. We slashed, burned, destroyed our empire of wood. We exploited our virgin agricultural land and created too often desertlike waste land that should never had been cleared of its forest cover."

Unfortunately, but understandably, land clearing was carried too far. There was no guidance: many settlers were novices in agriculture and did not know the difference between good and poor land. The forest was an enemy to get rid of. In too many areas the trees were felled with no thought of the suitability of the soil for cultivation, and never with a thought about future crops of trees.

But our pioneer farm settler had a partner in this saga of exploitation, the pioneer lumberman. The railways had opened up the country and timber had acquired added value. The lumberman came, often operating on sand plain areas covered with pine. The lumberman knew the value of timber, it was his business. He knew too, or should have known, that trees were a renewable resource. His only objective was to

E.C. Drury, former Premier of Ontario

get the best of the timber out as cheaply as possible.
Left behind was a mass of debris and waste, prime
fuel for fires which eventually destroyed the thin
covering of humus along with the seeds and
seedlings which could have produced a new forest
. . . only barren desertlike lands remained. During
the second half of the 1800s, millions upon millions of
board feet of timber was mined from the forests of
Ontario, an attack which gave no thought to future
forests.

The squared-timber boom continued until the last
decade of the 1800s when the big timber trade rapidly
diminished. By 1911, the last raft left Lake Ontario for
Quebec. An era had ended.

*Land-clearing in 18th century
New Brunswick*

Chapter 2 **Richardson's Roots**

The Richardson Musical group

A wisp of an early evening breeze fluttered across the town's park carrying with it the quiet laughter and murmured conversations of gentlemen and their ladies as they casually promenaded the paths to the town's auditorium. It was the summer of 1894.

Flyers tacked on lamp posts around town during the past week announced that

"SIMS RICHARDS AND FAMILY presents an evening of popular melodies. The instrumental charm of this string ensemble will grace you with an evening of classical and popular renditions. An historical oration will be presented during intermission."

This talented group of four young ladies under the direction of their father were from a family of five girls and three boys. The father, whose real name was Samuel Richardson, was skilled in music but, as a more stable support for his large family, was also skilled as a carpenter. He had noted that his children had natural musical talent. Through lessons and home training, each daughter (Ella, Evangeline, Louisa, and Laura) had been instructed in playing a stringed instrument. Within the heart and soul of their father was a spirit restless to entertain. Through summer months and at other times in the year, using the stage name of Sims Richards, Samuel and his daughters could be found performing in towns across Ontario and the provinces bordering the eastern seaboard. The usual "historical oration" given during intermissions was a lecture on the glories of the British Empire.

FROM LONDON TOWN TO TORONTO

Searching the pages of the family bible it appears that the Baptist parish of St. Margarets in London, England was a focal point for this branch of the

Richardsons, as many of them were married and buried from St. Margarets. The earliest testimony of marriage in the family bible recorded the nuptials of George Richardson and Elizabeth Burroughs at St. Margarets, Westminster on January 20, 1777. More entries document the fact that the portals of St. Margarets witnessed the coming and going of Richardsons. Almost a hundred years later, the trend was interrupted as inscribed by a carefully penned notice telling the reader that on March 16, 1869 in St. Marks church, Kensington, Samuel Richardson and Charlotte Susannah Good were married. Not long after their marriage, Sam and Charlotte boarded ship and emigrated to Canada.

Charlotte Susannah Richardson

Settling in the village of Rosseau in the Muskoka district of Ontario, Sam plied his carpentry skills as he and Charlotte went about raising a family and involving themselves in the parish life of the Church of the Redeemer. Their firstborn, George, arrived in June the next year. By the early 1880s, the family had grown to five children with the births of Ella, Evangeline, Louisa, and Laura. Confident of finding more opportunities in Toronto, the Richardsons packed up their belongings and headed for the city, finding a home in a midtown neighbourhood of Toronto not far from the Bloor-Bathurst Street inter-section. By the start of the 1890s, three more children had been added to the family scene, Ethel, Sidney, and the youngest born November 12, 1890 and christened Arthur Herbert.

As evidenced by a yellowed promotion flyer found in the family files, the city did afford Sam with more opportunities to indulge his talents in music and theatrics.

The musical Richardson household was often filled with the joys and tears of the lives of large families. But tragedy struck as the father took ill and died in 1902. Survival became a paramount concern for the family, even though the oldest children, now young adults, were working. It was decided that Arthur Herbert, who was then 12, would complete his pri-mary schooling and go to work.

Cathy Richardson, Arthur Herbert's daughter, recalls her father telling her that he worked at odd jobs

Herbert Richardson in choir, front row left

during the day and took his high school education in evening courses at Meisterschaft, a well-known, privately run school. "I was not allowed to do school work on Sunday," Cathy recalls her father saying. The Baptist faith was strong in the Richardson household. "Dad once expressed that he had seriously considered entering the ministry." This moral side of Arthur Herbert's character was often mirrored in his work ethics throughout his life.

THE WHITES

Mrs. Henry White at 90

For years Arthur Herbert was in and out of Ontario's Bruce Peninsula during the summer months. His first visit would have been around 1907 when he was 17. One of his jaunts was a hike from Wiarton to Tobermory during which he slept the nights in farmers' barns, followed each day by the sights and sounds of this nature's wonderland. During his sorties along the Bruce, Arthur Herbert became acquainted with the Henry White family, whose farm was near Mar, a small hamlet north of Wiarton. He stayed with the Whites on occasions during the summers. When the Whites had their eighth child, a boy, they named him Arthur Herbert. In later years, Richardson and his wife looked upon Arthur Herbert White's children as their "grandchildren". In what seemed to be a tradition, Arthur Herbert White and his wife, Dora, named their first boy Arthur Herbert.

TEACHER AND PREACHER!

Having matriculated from Meisterschaft and needing a break from the stress of working during the day and attending school in the evening, Richardson spent a winter with the Whites. In February of that year, a one-room school near Tobermory lost its teacher, and Arthur Herbert was persuaded to take the position. Combined with a burgeoning skill for teaching and the appeal of life in this rural area, Richardson benefited from this "break". One of his pastimes was paddling and investigating the nearby Pat and Ella River in a birchbark canoe bought from a local Native.

One summer, during his university years at McMaster, Arthur Herbert added another dimension to his teaching experience. According to Ken Higgs, former General Manager of the Metropolitan Toronto and Region Conservation Authority, "Mr. Richardson on Sundays during that summer took on the pastoral service as a lay preacher for a church near Thornbury."

During his pre-university days, Arthur Herbert, still helping the home finances and building funds to attend university, had found a job with the engineering office attached to the City of Toronto's roads department. He held on to this job as he gathered the necessary funds to help see him through McMaster and the following two intervening years before heading to Harvard.

TOWARDS HIGHER EDUCATION — McMASTER AND HARVARD

His religious affirmation was probably one reason for Arthur Herbert choosing to attend the Baptist-run McMaster University in the fall semester of 1913. McMaster (re-located in Hamilton in 1930) was located then in a Romanesque Revival style, red sandstone building on Toronto's Bloor street immediately east of today's Varsity Stadium. (This building presently houses the Royal Conservatory of Music.) The five-storey structure, built in 1881, was said to be the tallest building in Toronto at that time. Named McMaster Hall after its wealthy benefactor, Senator William McMaster, it was in fact the home of a theological school, the Toronto Baptist College. It was granted a university charter on April 22, 1887.

Besides being a bright student, Richardson's athletics skills earned him a place on the University's track team. In intercollegiate competition of the 1915-16 season, running under the maroon and grey colours of McMaster, he won both the Challenger Medal and the McNaught Cup.

After graduating with his BA (Hon.) degree in the spring of 1916, Arthur Herbert, encouraged by the Dean, returned to McMaster to earn his Master's degree in Biology. In the ensuing two years he retained his connection with the University as a member of the executive committee of the University's Literary Society. On November 12, 1918, the day after

Arthur Herbert Richardson at 27 years in 1917

McMaster University Track team 1916-1917

the Armistice of World War I was declared, Richardson celebrated his 28th birthday at Harvard University. He had been there since September, having entered on a scholarship to study Silvicultural Science in the Department of Applied Biology. His long-time interests and determination to learn more about Nature's outdoor resources, particularly the forest, had now taken on a career-directed influence. Cathy Richardson tells of her father's welcome to Harvard:

"Dad told me that the Harvard professor he studied under was delighted to have him as a student. For one reason, Dad was his only student. If Dad hadn't come, the professor had no class and possibly no job."

LOVE BLOSSOMS IN BOSTON

Romance blossomed while Arthur Herbert was attending Harvard, when he met an attractive and talented undergraduate, Winifred Symington, who was attending Emerson College in Boston. "My mother," Cathy recalls, "used to tell the story of how she and Dad would spend a pleasant afternoon canoeing on the Charles River while he serenaded her with his Spanish guitar."

Winifred Florence Symington, until late teens, grew up in Dundalk, Ontario. Her father, Joseph Symington was the town's well-respected CPR agent. Winifred's parents enrolled her at the Ontario Ladies College in Whitby for her high school education and then at Emerson College in Boston where she graduated with a Dramatic Arts degree. Daughter Cathy admits that,

Arthur Herbert Richardson at 26 years in 1916

"I never pictured Father as a great romantic, but in our family treasures I have a booklet of poems composed by Dad in 1919 and dedicated to Mom. The verses are typed on hand-made paper and bound by a ribbon to form the booklet."

As future years demonstrated, Arthur Herbert had no difficulty in turning out imaginative phrases in a prosaic or poetic form.

With his Harvard Master's degree added to his résumé, Arthur Herbert returned to Toronto and was hired by the Forestry Branch of Ontario's Department of Lands and Forests.

Winifred and Arthur Herbert were married at High Park United Church in Toronto on June 22, 1922. Turning down a job offer in Montreal as a stage director for one of the city's theatrical companies, Winifred turned her attention to directing the activities of their home and social life. However, she did continue her interest in music and, being an accomplished pianist, she used her talent to teach piano from their home.

CATHY RICHARDSON'S STORY

In 1938 a historical family event took place in the life of Winifred and Arthur Herbert. With both now in their late forties and no children, they decided to adopt a child. Their blessing was an eight-month-old baby, Catherine Ann.

"Dad was 47 when I was adopted but I never thought of either of my parents as being old. He was always the one out in the backyard stomping down the snow to make a skating rink. My parents were the ones who took me and neighbourhood kids to the Santa Claus parade while their parents stayed home. When I entered university my father was getting ready to retire. I must admit that when I graduated and no one else's father was near retirement, it crossed my mind that he must be older. Age was never discussed, and it wasn't until the last two years of his life that he physically slowed down, but not his mind. He was incredible; he never lost interest in things about him."

"Although Mother would have preferred to live in a small town, Dad embraced Toronto. Frequent trips on Sunday afternoon to High Park were a joy for me.

Winifred Florence (Symington) Richardson at 18

Dad felt that there were too few parks and he believed that parks should be easily accessible to families."

SUMMER CONSERVATION CAMPS

"The first summers holidays were spent at a house at Angus, at Ontario's Forestry Station [Ontario's Ministry of Natural Resources Seed Extraction Station]. Though very young I have strong impressions of spacious land and beautifully kept lawns, huge pools with bridges between them. When Dad left Lands and Forests in 1944 for the (Conservation Branch) Department of Planning and Development we spent our summers at the various Conservation Survey camp sites (base camps from which the surveys of specific watersheds were carried out under Richardson's overall direction). Our 'home' was a canvas-roof structure covering two or three tent floors supporting wooden walls with windows and doors that had been assembled together to make a 'family unit'. It was called 'The Palace'. Mother prepared the breakfast and lunch and we had dinner at the main dining tent with the staff. When located near a river or lake, I was never allowed to go swimming alone or when my mother was looking after me. She didn't like the water as the result of a fright she experienced as a

Camp dining tent

child. My dad was a fabulous swimmer.

"I had a library card for every town that was nearby. Mom and I would accompany the camp manager when he went to town. He would buy groceries and supplies, and we would go to the library.

"During the summer Mother would be visited by her friends and cousins and I by one or two girl friends.

"One summer we were camped in a farmer's field bordering the Nith River near Baden in Mennonite country. There was a Mennonite church nearby and on a Sunday one could hear hymns being sung by the congregation with verve and forte. This impressed Dad, for not only did he love to sing but he had a fine tenor voice. So without Mom and myself, he would go off to the Mennonite service and join the congregation, singing to his heart's content. That was the year I tried to teach a Mennonite girl how to play cards, not knowing that it wasn't an acceptable practice for them. I was totally amazed on learning that the girl had never been to a movie."

"Those were wonderful years. By the time I reached my 15th birthday Dad felt that I was too old to be living in 'men's' camps, so my summers were spent elsewhere."

THE FOUR-SEATER

Arthur Herbert, in the minds of some of his associates and staff, demonstrated certain autocratic tendencies that verged on a regal posture. A former staff person, with a touch of wry humour, shared this story of an incident that took place during the South Nation River survey in the Prescott region. The camp had been located on a site just east of Prescott.

"We set up at a place alongside of an old canal system that is now under water because of the St. Lawrence Seaway. The whole terrain was made up of excavated material dug out of the canal.

"It was a mixture of shale and clay. Just bloody impossible to dig. For the camp, we had a big 'four-holer' privy that we transported around. As part of the work force, we always had a bunch of high school kids who did the 'flunky' jobs. Their first job was to dig a massive pit for this privy to sit over. It took them two days to get this damned privy set up. When the camp was near ready with

'The Palace' in place, we awaited Arthur Herbert's regal visit for inspection. On the day of inspection, Arthur Herbert arrived, walked into the 'Palace', strode to the main front window, paused, looked, and pointed to a structure that intruded on the view from the window. 'What's that?' The camp chief stammered, 'That's the latrine.' Turning, Arthur Herbert snapped, 'I want that moved!' It took the poor kids another three days to dig a new hole and move the privy out of view."

Cathy recalls, "Dad at times could be singularly minded. When it came time to buying a cottage, in this case at Sauble Beach on Lake Huron, Mother was given the choice of any cottage that was for sale. However, that was the only choice she had. No other beach was acceptable to Dad. He purchased a cottage owned by Mr. Thompson whose daughter Diane married Ted Sutter. The Sutters both worked for the Metro Conservation Authority (MTRCA) and today they have the cottage next to ours."

Cottage at Sauble Beach

Diane Sutter tells of Arthur Herbert's enjoyment in the company of children. "My daughter, Nancy used to go walking with Mr. Richardson in the mornings when she was a little tyke. He would hold her hand as they strolled along a beach road while she questioned him about many things. Charles Sauriol, author and conservationist of fame described Richardson in his senior years as "the kindest and most patient man I ever saw."

After her mother died in 1977, Cathy sold the family home but kept the cottage.

THE FINAL SCENE

"Friends called Dad 'Herb'. (On a formal basis, 'Mr. Richardson' or 'Arthur Herbert' was common.) Dad was guarded about telling his age and only revealed it publicly on two occasions. By permission from the Department he worked to his 70th year. On the occasion of his retirement, he amusingly related that when he moved from Lands and Forests to Planning and Development his age had been erroneously recorded as one year younger than he was, in fact, he was now 71.

"The other occasion was when he turned 80. He was proud to have reached that age and freely told everyone. Nevertheless, when I asked him a year later how old he was, he replied 'A lady never asks and a gentleman never tells.'

"Dad felt that the Government was not doing enough in conservation management. In spite of all the watershed surveys that had been done and the recommendations made, it took Hurricane Hazel to stir up more and immediate action. (In his book, *Conservation for the People*, Richardson noted that the effect of Hurricane Hazel activated two major changes: the merger of adjoining authorities in the formation of the Metropolitan Toronto and Region Conservation Authority (MTRCA); and the planning for a co-ordinated flood-control and water-conservation plan for the whole region.) He found it frustrating working for government. Politics disturbed him. After appearing at sessions in support of his minister, he would come home late sometimes disappointed with the outcome. But the next day he would set out determined to try again, using a different approach. He was resilient in that way.

"In 1946, Dad collaborated with Alexander W. Galbraith in publishing a book entitled *Trees We Should Know.* It contained 233 original photographic studies by Galbraith with the description by Dad. In one of the first edition copies, he wrote this inscription to me:

'Towards the end of the eternal journey only this is necessary . . . The Memory of Love!' "

A.H. Richardson at retirement

Chapter 3 **The National Scene**

FORESTRY AND CONSERVATION IN CONGRESS!

From the last half of the 1800s and into the second decade of the 1900s, tens of thousands of hectares of Canada's forests were tragically consumed by fire. A pall of smoke hung across the country from burning forests caused by nature's lightning. Added to this were the wild fires resulting from the careless burning of logging slash; the incendiary sparks from firepots of steam trains; the brush burning and lunch fires of railway work gangs; the felling and torching of trees and debris by settlers who, in their self-interest, were clearing land for farming, mine sites, and communities; and finally, the scorched-earth fire set by native Indians and others to create conditions favourable for blueberry crops. Much of the hardwood timber removed for settlement reasons was used to feed a profitable potash industry where thousands of tons extracted from the hardwood ash were shipped through the Great Lakes system to overseas markets.

Forest fire in Northern Ontario

Witnessing these destructive actions, concerned farmers, politicians, conservationists, and lumbermen began to realize that the forests of the North American continent were indeed limited and exhaustible. Eight years before the birth of Arthur Herbert Richardson, the City of Cincinnati, Ohio hosted North America's first major conference on forestry. This 1882 gathering, formally titled the American Forestry Congress, was quickly dubbed "The First Parliament of Forestry in North America". It was here that the Conservation Movement became a socio-political phenomenon. Due to the impetus created at the Congress, North America entered what was termed the "classical age of conservation".

Three delegates were sent by the Ontario Government: the Fruit Growers' Association of Ontario, the newly established Ontario Agricultural College of Guelph, and an entomologist.

WASTE, WASTE, WASTE

At the conference (1882), the American Association for the Advancement of Science joined the common theme, that the consumption and waste of the country's forests greatly exceeded the restoration ability of nature. They maintained that the combination of wasteful cutting practices, forest fires, poor wood utilization, and poor land-clearing procedures was eradicating North America's forests. Ecologists bemoaned the fact that damage to the environment, to nature's balance and beauty, was causing forest soil erosion and harm to wildlife and its habitat. From a global perspective, one speaker cited the disastrous conditions in China where regions once covered with forest were now wastelands.

A Canadian, James Little, a successful Quebec lumberman and exporter to the U.S., was a keynote speaker. Governments, he said, were using timber resources for political advantages and swallowing the resulting revenues into their general funds while spending little on forestry. (This accusation was still a complaint at the 1980 Forestry Congress held in Toronto.) Turning to his fellow lumbermen, Little charged them with wasteful logging practices and

Sir Henry Joly de Lotbinière

Bernard Edward Fernow

short-sighted profit motives. The delegates representing the Fruit Growers' Association of Ontario were struck by the content of this message and the similarity to conditions existing in their home province.

In August of the same year, the Congress reconvened in Montreal and was hosted by the Canadian government. Supporting the concerns of Little at this meeting was Sir Henry Joly de Lotbinière. The well-respected Lotbinière had a better-than-ordinary appreciation of forestry. He had established on his land near Quebec City a tree plantation and in adjoining forest stands was practising a form of "sustained-yield" management.

The only graduate forester at the meeting was a young German, Bernard Edward Fernow, who would play a major role in the forestry debate in the U.S. and Canada. Fernow's review of the papers presented at the conference was critical, commenting that tree planting, arboriculture, and forest-fire protection were the dominant subjects, noting that the ideas of how to preserve and manage the forest resources were scarcely discussed. For most at the meeting, Fernow made a favourable impression. For many, he was the first professional forester they had ever heard.

The summation statement called for the implementation of European silviculture practices, applied forest ecology, a system of classifying land as suitable either to farming or forestry, and tree planting. It berated existing poor logging practices, the wasting of forest lands by settlers, and the senseless destruction of forests by fires.

AFTER THE CONGRESS

Positive fall-out from the Congress began to occur within a year. In Ontario the Department of Agriculture set up the position of Clerk of Forestry whose prime duty was to inform and educate the public, particularly farmers, on the care of their woodlots. For the job, the Department named Robert W. Phipps, apple farmer and journalist. Phipps travelled southern Ontario and corresponded with farmers, urging them to stop the over-clearing of forested land, especially land unsuited for agriculture.

In Guelph at the Ontario College of Agriculture, their delegate to the Congress, Professor William Brown had returned home to set up a lecture course on forestry along with setting up study plots and ornamental forestry demonstrations.

Phipps' successor as Chief Clerk, Aubrey White, wrote a memorandum to the Commissioner of Crown Lands outlining his plan for better fire-protection procedure. As a result, in 1885, the Ontario Government passed a statute entitled ''An Act to Preserve the Forest from Destruction by Fire''.

In the same year, the Canadian Government set aside ten square miles (26 km²) in the Alberta Rockies that were the nucleus of Banff National Park. Back in Ontario, a letter had been written by Alexander Kirkwood to his boss, T.B. Paradee, MPP, the Commissioner for Crown Lands for Ontario, detailing the setting aside of 400 000 acres (16 900 ha) of forest reserve as a ''National Forest and Park'' to be given the name ''Algonkin Park'', named after one of the great North American Indian nations.

The Ontario Government, with Kirkwood as Chairman, set up a Royal Commission on Forest Reservation and a National Park. The final report made several recommendations for the establishment of a ''public park and forest reservation, fish and game preserve, health resort and pleasure ground for the benefit, advantage and enjoyment of the people of the Province.'' In the 1893 session of the Ontario Legislature, an Act was passed and Algonquin Park came into being.

FORESTRY IS BORN!

In 1897, the Federal Department of the Interior appointed a Commissioner of Forestry, J.H. Morgan, one of the Montreal Conference organizers. Morgan was to experience much frustration as his sensible and progressive plans were ignored time and again by his deputy minister. Morgan was calling for regulations against indiscriminate logging, training centres for would-be foresters, and fire-control measurements.

Forester and land owner discuss woodlot improvement

A well-managed woodlot and harvested firewood

CANADIAN FORESTRY ASSOCIATION

In Ottawa two years later, the Federal Government made a key move in its forestry program with the appointment of Elihu Stewart as Dominion Chief Inspector of Timber and Forestry. Forest protection against fires and reforestation was the key issue across Canada. Stewart was to build the Canadian Forestry Service that played a fundamental role in forest research. Pertinent to our story, however, he organized a group of lumber barons, bankers, businessmen, educators, and politicians into a lay-men's association known as the Canadian Forestry Association. Joining Stewart in setting up the CFA was Thomas Southworth, the manager of the Brockville *Recorder* and, at the time, first Director of the Ontario Bureau of Forestry.

By March of 1890, the CFA held its first meeting with Sir Henri Joly de Lotbinière as Chairman. The CFA's prime objective was informing the public of the value of Canada's forest resource and the absolute necessity of protecting it from fire and other destructive agencies.

Leached and eroded ruined soil

THE NEED . . . PROFESSIONAL FORESTERS!

Although their intentions were commendable, it became evident that the members of the CFA could only discuss forestry matters in a general way. The Association knew that there was a need for a scientifically trained staff knowledgeable in all aspects of tending the reproduction and development of the forest environment that would require a credible plan of management. They had exposure to one such scientist in Montreal during the 1882 American Forestry Congress in the person of Bernard Fernow. (By 1886 Fernow would be made the first Chief of the Division of Forestry in the U.S. Department of Agriculture.) At the Congress, one of the recommendations called for greater emphasis on forests in the curricula of agricultural schools and universities.

Active discussion on establishing a Forestry School in Canada was being promoted by the CFA. In its 1902 annual meeting, attended by members from across Canada, Southworth stated, "It is evident to thoughtful men that the time has arrived when we need more highly trained men in our forests," meaning men trained to study them on a scientific basis. A year later, Fernow (who had just established at Cornell the first forestry school of collegiate rank on the continent) was invited to give a series of lectures at Kingston's Queen's University.

Ranging over every aspect of Canadian forestry, the lectures strongly stimulated the movements for establishing forestry schools at Canadian universities. Emphasizing the need for professionalism in forest management, the Ontario Bureau of Forestry in 1904, with Southworth as Director, hired its first full-time professional forester, Judson F. Clark. A graduate of Guelph's Ontario College of Agriculture (1896), and a student of Dr. Fernow at Cornell.

CANADA'S FIRST FORESTRY SCHOOL

Over at Guelph's Ontario College of Agriculture, it was apparent that this college was interested in expanding its work in forestry. The year before, E.J. Zavitz, a McMaster graduate with a postgraduate degree in forestry from the University of Michigan, was appointed to give instruction in forestry. The Ontario Experimental Union had strongly urged the Government to "establish at the earliest possible date a school of forestry. . . ." (Until this took place, all Forestry graduates working in Canada would be the products of European or U.S. universities, such as Cornell, Yale, and Michigan.) On the national scene, the CFA again at its 1904 annual meeting called on the Ontario government to "make an appropriate grant for the operation of a provincial school or schools of forestry." Two years later in Ottawa, H. Joly de Lotbinière, in his presidential address at the national Forestry Convention, expressed the urgency to establish a Canadian forestry school "where our young men may be enabled to receive a forestry education of a character suited to the needs of our country."

Meanwhile, discussion continued on which university would establish a forestry school. Queen's and Toronto were both in the running, with Guelph making strong hints of its interest. Following much debate that included a Royal Commission, the recommendations endorsed Toronto as the appropriate site and on February 14, 1907, the Board of Governors at the University of Toronto, approved the establishment of a Faculty of Forestry. On March 28, the

Seedlings for reforestation

appointment of Bernard E. Fernow as Dean was approved. A year later a forestry department was in place at the University of New Brunswick. By 1910 in Quebec City, a founding member of the Canadian Forestry Association, Professor J.C.K. Laflamme, set up a Forestry school at Laval University.

"A NEED TO MEET"

In a letter to A.H.D. Ross, the assistant to Doctor Fernow, Fredrick Jacombe, a member of the Department of the Interior, Forestry Branch in Ottawa called for the formation of a Canada-wide association of technically trained foresters and officials holding prominent forestry positions. After discussing the letter with Dean Fernow, action was recommended to be taken in Montreal following the 9th annual meeting of the Canadian Forestry Association on Thursday, March 12th, 1908.

CANADIAN SOCIETY OF FOREST ENGINEERS IS BORN

On the evening of March 12th, at Montreal's Board of Trade, five foresters met to discuss the formation of a professional body of foresters. Chaired by Dr. Fernow, the others included Ellwood Wilson, Chief Forester of Quebec's Laurentide Company; Gustave Piché, Forester, Department of Lands and Forests, Quebec; Abraham Knechtel, who would become Chief Forester, Dominion Parks Branch; and Fred Jacombe, Technical Assistant, Forestry Branch, Department of Interior, Ottawa. Jacombe, selected as organizing committee chairman, worked into the early hours of the morning to complete a draft of a tentative constitution.

The following day, March 13th, joined by other foresters including Ed Zavitz of the Ontario Dept. of Agriculture, the group accepted the draft and elected Dr. Fernow as president. As to what name should be adopted, the founding members had some trouble deciding. In the end, the chosen name was the Canadian Society of Forest Engineers. (In 1950, the name was changed to the Canadian Institute of Forestry.)

Seed extracting Plant at Angus, Ontario

RICHARDSON AND THE FORESTRY CHRONICLE

Logo of Canadian Institute of Forestry

In the early 1920s a new figure appeared at the meeting of the CSFE: Arthur Herbert Richardson. A recent post-graduate from Yale and a Forester with Ontario's Forestry Branch, Richardson had no doubt been encouraged to get involved with the Society by his boss, E.J. Zavitz, one of its founding members. During the CSFE's 1924 annual meeting, there had been some loosely directed discussion to publish its own "technical organ" to replace the *Journal of Forestry*, the publication of the American Society of American Foresters which the CSFE members were receiving. Encouraged by the Society's executive, led by Dr. C.D. Howe, Dean of the Faculty of Forestry at Toronto and soon to be president of the CSFE, Richardson had been diligently working behind the scenes designing and developing a News-Letter. Ken Fenson, in his book on the history of the Canadian Institute of Forestry described what took place

". . . in 1925 *The Forestry Chronicle* in bound mimeograph form,. . . literally burst on the scene."

Richardson, as its founder and first editor, played a vital role in the first nine years of this national publication. *The Forestry Chronicle* in 1929 became a printed publication. Through the years, the research, development, and management practices of the science of forestry in Canada have been revealed in the pages of this credible publication.

The following year with the resignation of the secretary, Dr. Howe, in the role of President, appointed Richardson to the job. Commenting on the incident, Richardson was puzzled but pleased.

Cover of Forest Chronicle
April 1991

"I don't know what prompted him to ask me, but I did wonder at the time, that with so many of his own graduates in and around Toronto, why he should have selected a forester who had taken his training elsewhere [McMaster and Yale]. Frankly, I was pleased, as I had a great respect for Dr. Howe and learned to appreciate his many fine qualities."

During the 1926 annual meeting in Toronto, Dr. Howe was queried if the constitution gave him the power to appoint a new secretary. Dr. Howe explained that the constitution had no provision for such an appointment, so he consulted with members of the executive who readily approved the selection of Richardson. As Ken Fenson commented in his book, ". . . fortunately for the CSFE, Richardson became a tower of strength and a prodigious worker for the Society and for the advancement of forestry in Canada."

FORESTRY AND PUBLIC PERCEPTION: THEN

What was the state of forestry in Canada at the beginning of the 1930s? In a *Forestry Chronicle* editorial, Richardson stated,

"Never before in Canada has so much interest been taken in the proper care and development of our forests. But who is responsible for this country-wide awakening cannot be said. No one group nor organization can take all the credit, but certainly the steadily growing body of professional foresters in Canada has had some influence."

Nevertheless, the advancement of the forest conservation principle in 1929 was not striking a responsive chord that would lead to meaningful national action. In the words of Dr. Howe, Dean of the Faculty of Forestry,

"We have been talking about forestry for over 40 years in this country and as yet we have no definitely stated or legislatively enacted forest policy on the part of the Dominion Government, or that of any province, based on the fundamental of continuous production."

The reason for this, said Dr. Howe, was the general conception that forests must be cleared to make room for farms; that the standing timber is inexhaustible, and of necessity, foresters have devoted most of their energies to fire protection. Added to these reasons was the economic restriction that only high-grade lumber could be profitably marketed. Therefore, waste was unavoidable and sustained forest management economically impossible.

In December of 1929, Richardson wrote in *The Chronicle* that,

"for some time there has been insistent demand. . . that the
Dominion Government formulate and carry on a definite federal
forest policy."

He pointed out that the Canadian Chamber of Commerce had asked the Canadian Forestry Association, with only a small percentage of foresters as members, to submit a policy statement in regards to Canadian forestry problems. Richardson said it was humiliating that the CFA had been asked to do this instead of the CSFE. Just as disturbing was the observation of a well-known businessman expressing surprise that forestry could be considered a technical profession. It would be another 20 years before the Canada Forestry Act was passed.

In a positive vein, Richardson wrote in a 1929 issue of *The Forestry Chronicle* that,

"The Canadian Society of Forest Engineers consists of a body of
men whose education, work, and aspiration combine to identify
them as active agents on behalf of the perpetuation of Canada's
forest. The accomplishment of the Society as a whole toward the
continuation in a profitable state of this important factor in the
industrial life of Canada is the sum of the works of its members."

Citing examples of this influence by CSFE members, Richardson pointed to E.J. Zavitz's role as head of the improved Ontario Fire Protection Service; R.H. Campbell's success in establishing a Dominion Forest Products Laboratory; and the effective role played by CSFE President Clyde Leavitt in helping the Premier of New Brunswick frame a forest policy for the province.

CSFE — SOUTHERN ONTARIO SECTION FORMED

In January 1930, Richardson, along with Dean Howe, Ed Zavitz, Frank Sharpe, and Steve Brodie (the latter two were from the Ontario Department of Lands and Forests), signed a petition that was presented at a General Executive meeting of the CSFE in Ottawa seeking the authority to establish a Southern Ontario Section. This was granted along with a similar request by the Ottawa Valley Section. There was no follow-up by either Section until four years later.

Logs floating downstream from a logging area

On a pleasant June evening in 1934, a meeting of Ontario CSFE members was held in the common room at the Angus Seed Extraction Plant. Dr. Howe chaired the meeting, and recorded in *The Forestry Chronicle* was the following:

"Richardson raised the question of an Ontario Section and pointed out that a petition had been passed on by the (CSFE) Executive ratifying the formation of a Southern Ontario Section, but up to the present, it had not functioned to any great extent. It was decided to revive this section, and then Dr. Howe called for nominations for the positions of chairman and secretary. It was the unanimous decision that these positions be filled respectively by Messrs. Ben Avery and Professor R.C. Hosie (Faculty of Forestry, Toronto)."

FORESTRY LEADERSHIP, WHERE IS IT?

By 1934, the CSFE and CFA seemed to be occupied with a concern for the lack of "Forestry Leadership". Several prominent CSFE members, led by Dr. C.D. Howe, along with Richardson, W.A. Delahey, and E.H. Finlayson had become disenchanted with the programs of the CFA headed by Robson Black. They charged that the management of its programs lacked meaningful forestry education content and its magazine exhibited a trend towards unacceptable commercialism.

In July, Richardson wrote to the president of the CFA stating:

"As you probably know the members of this society (CSFE) represent 90% of the men who are carrying on forestry work in Canada. For the most part they have confined themselves to the technical side of the problem and have left the work of popular propaganda in this field to the Canadian Forestry Association. I regret to say that in this respect we feel that to a large extent the Association has betrayed its trust."

After a special meeting that included both CFA and CSFE, the final act in the wrangle was the CFA Board of Directors' decision to support Black's action. Four years later Black was invited to address the CSFE members. In his concluding remarks, Black expressed the hope that the two organizations would again work together hand in hand and that, in his opinion, the past differences had been misunderstandings rather than basic conflicts of opinion.

THE NEED FOR A PERMANENT SECRETARY

Meanwhile discussion had been going on pertaining to the need to establish a permanent and paid secretary for the CSFE. The growing work load was demanding more and more of Richardson's time. In the debate that followed, Walter ab Yberg, Chairman of the Executive Committee for Quebec, the Maritime Provinces, and Newfoundland, deploring the lack of involvement by many members in the CSFE cause, gave an unsolicited testimonial of Richardson's contribution.

"There are professional men who have given many years of untiring effort in trying to raise the standard of the Society. . . . We have a secretary, and a very worthy one, Mr. Richardson, who has repeatedly filled this position. You must all admit that he is one of those members who does not require any 'pep' serum treatment, and I desire to move right here and now that the deepest appreciation of this Society be extended to Mr. Richardson in recognition of his splendid service. I marvel at how much he has done in return for the grand remuneration of $2 per month. . . ."

On May 1, 1935 Ellwood Wilson took office as the first part-time paid secretary and editor of *The Forestry Chronicle* earlier in the year.

A FORESTER IS A FORESTER . . . IS A FORESTER . . . IS A . . .

In *The Forestry Chronicle*'s February issue of 1935, Richardson correctly interpreted the public mind that the technical forester (university graduate, science-trained forester) lacked a professional status similar to engineers, doctors, dentists. He declared that,

"technical foresters in Canada are suffering from an exaggerated sense of modesty. We have been too satisfied with our achievements and most of us are perfectly willing to settle into a comfortable job and let someone else instruct the public at large to the purposes of forestry and what foresters really are."

Advocating the title "Forest Engineer" be adopted, he urged the use of MCSFE after members' names, and encouraged members to write articles for magazines and seek out opportunities to give popular or technical addresses on forestry. In 1950, members of the profession in Ontario were recognized as Registered Professional Foresters (RPF) through the enactment of a private member's bill. The designation "RPF" now had an official professional status.

At the 1936 annual meeting held in Ottawa, Arthur Herbert was elected Vice-President. It was at this meeting that his outstanding contribution to the cause of forestry in many fields was publicly recognized by the CSFE. Over the signature of the president, W.A. Delahey, and the secretary, Ellwood Wilson, the scroll read as follows:

"for the great service to the Society covering a period of ten years during which he founded and edited *The Forestry Chronicle* and served as Secretary. For his work in reforestation, for his bulletins, lectures, and popular articles on general forestry, for his work for 16 years as special lecturer at OAC, for his organization of the reforestation work for the Ontario Forestry Branch, for his establishment of seed collecting station (Angus) and the improvement of seed extraction techniques, and for the organization of county and municipal forests."

RICHARDSON REINSTATED AS EDITOR

What was a well-operating organization under the guiding hand of Ellwood Wilson, appeared to falter badly when Wilson became ill. Some members suggested discontinuing publishing *The Forestry Chronicle*.

However, with detractors and supporters debating, Richardson was asked to take over as editor for one last fling, in January 1937. With the appointment of a new editor in 1939, Richardson was appointed Honourary Editor of Publications for the CSFE.

With the increasing work pressures of his "full-time" job with the Department of Lands and Forests, Arthur Herbert's high-profile activities with the CSFE began to fade. He kept in touch through the Southern Ontario Section, and chaired that section for the 1941-42 year. When the CSFE changed its name to the Canadian Institute of Forestry in 1950, Arthur Herbert looked on as an ordinary member.

HONOURED BY MCGILL UNIVERSITY

Following his retirement in February 1962, Arthur Herbert and Winifred were invited to Montreal for the Convocation ceremonies at McGill University. On a pleasant spring day, the Dean of the Faculty of Agriculture, H.G. Dion, rose and read the assembled students, professors, and guests the following citation dated May 13th, 1962.

A.H. Richardson receiving his Doctorate at McGill University in 1962

"I have the honour to present Arthur Herbert Richardson, distinguished Canadian conservationist, in order that you may confer on him the degree of Doctor of Law, *honoris causa*. Mr. Richardson has been responsible, more than any other single man, for the development of conservation and flood-control programmes and policies in Canada beginning with his role in the pioneering of the Ganaraska Watershed near Port Hope, and culminating in the establishment of 37 Conservation Authorities in Ontario, which are a model for co-ordinating the interests of regional and local government in dealing with these problems. Mr. Richardson's vision and leadership in the field of Conservation earned an international reputation which is the greatest tribute to his success.

"As a biologist with imagination, a forester with insight, an engineer with a sense of real values, and a man with a burning concern for the well-being of his fellow men, young and old, he does us honour by becoming one of our distinguished graduates."

Conservation Through Scouting — The Youth Movement

Chapter 4

Lord Baden-Powell — founder of Scouting

Baden-Powell and possibly one of the first Girl Guides in Canada

Although Richardson was actively involved with the Boy Scout movement for over 30 years, records existing prior to 1923 give no hint of him having a link with Scouting, and certainly not as a boy. By the time General Lord Robert Baden-Powell's Boy Scout Movement had received its Royal Charter of Incorporation in 1910, Arthur Herbert was 20.

On a warm August 29th of that year, 10 000 people, 300 Scouts, and a bevy of dignitaries patiently waited at Toronto's Union Station to welcome the hero of Mafeking and Chief Scout of the World who was arriving from Winnipeg by the Canadian Pacific Railway train. He was coming to open the Canadian National Exhibition the next day. Two and a half hours behind schedule, the puffing train finally drew into the station. The reception groups hurried along to the parlour car to greet the distinguished guest while other passengers got off, including a patrol of 16 English Boy Scouts. The train emptied, but no Baden-Powell. A communication gaffe had happened. At no time during the time-consuming trip from Winnipeg had the Chief Scout been clued in on the grand preparations made for his reception at Union Station. The General, anxious to stretch his legs and "scout" the city, had left the train earlier at the Parkdale Station and made his way, partly by foot but mainly by "tram car", to his host's home in Rosedale. The host was waiting for him along with everyone else at Union Station.

Four months later on December 21, 1910, the Boy Scout Provincial Council for Ontario was chartered.

BOY SCOUTS AND FORESTRY!

Public interest in forestry matters had been aroused, particularly because of the destruction by forest fires, the most recent being during the hours of one day, October 4, 1922, that devastated Haileybury and area, destroying 6000 homes and claiming 40 lives. The Government's resumption of reforesting the sand-waste lands in Southern Ontario had prompted the interest in forestry by Ontario's Boy Scout Association. This seemed a natural interest for an organization whose young people spent so much of their activities in woodland settings. The Forestry Branch was approached by the Assistant Provincial Commissioner, Frank C. Irwin, and asked if they would consider setting up a series of lectures and activities on forestry as part of the Association's Gilwell Leadership Training program. In response, Zavitz directed Richardson to see what could be done. The concept fitted two major interests of Arthur Herbert that would be central in his work in forestry and conservation in the years ahead: one, the involvement of youth in the conservation movement; and two, the application of educational teaching technique and hands-on activities to teach conservation.

By the spring of 1924, Richardson had readied a program to teach forest conservation. He personally committed himself to present the course and launched it at the first permanent Scout Leadership training site at the recently acquired Ebor Park Camp that edged the bank of the Grand River near Brantford. Frank Irwin, who had earlier asked the Forestry Branch for help, was in charge. The appearance of Richardson at this course became an annual commitment and was the start of a long-time friendship between himself and Irwin.

In the ensuing years, he modified the program to deal with both forestry and conservation. In the 1924 Scout's Ontario Provincial Council's Annual Report, Richardson is lauded for his efforts in the training of Scout Leaders. From this time forward, the presence of Scouts, Guides, and other youth groups became a consistent part of Richardson's public demonstration programs on forestry and conservation.

RESTORE THE FORESTS

That same year, the Forestry Branch, with Zavitz as Provincial Forester and Richardson as the Branch's Forester and author, released Bulletin No. 1, "Forest Tree Planting". It was a booklet designed to encourage and guide municipalities, farmers, and private land-owners to reforest the areas that they owned. In its introduction, Richardson stated that, in Old Ontario, the area south of the Georgian Bay region, there was an estimated 8500 square miles (2 201 500 ha) of land *suited only* to tree growth, made up mostly of large contiguous sand barrens and sparsely wooded hills. However, a large amount was made up of smaller but widely distributed areas in good agricultural districts. These areas were either steep hillsides, rocky or grav-elly fields, or fields of extremely light soils.

In 1925, a Canada-wide "Save The Forest" campaign was launched by the Dominion Government. Litera-ture was distributed by Scouts throughout the provinces. In Ontario, under Richardson's influence, many Scout troops carried out tree planting exercises directed by Lands and Forests' Forestry Branch. Within the year, Ontario's Department of Education had passed a regulation establishing an annual Arbour Day each spring.

Scouts taking part in tree planting project

Trees for Schools

Recognizing the significance of Arbour Day as an educational opportunity to promote conservation and forestry through youth, and knowing the need for professional direction in handling tree planting, Richardson, with Zavitz's approval (Zavitz later became Deputy Minister of Forestry), wrote a Forestry Branch circular entitled "Trees For Schools". The booklet emphasized the use of trees and shrubbery to improve the aesthetic appearance of rural school property. In some cases, if the school property was large enough, a demonstration woodlot was established. The purpose was to show local farmers how abandoned areas of a farm could be beneficially used to grow trees.

In his book *Conservation For The People*, written nearly 50 years later, Richardson noted,

"For many years, the naturalists of Ontario — both professional and amateur — have tried to instill in the youth...a heightened regard for the complex relation between man, animals, and the landscape that we call nature. That their efforts have been successful is self-evident; today's youth can and do speak with knowledge and discernment about 'ecology', 'environmental factors' and 'recycling of waste'.

School children and adults in a planting project.

BOY SCOUT FORESTRY CAMP

Four years after his initial participation in the Ebor Camp program, Richardson devised a more ambitious program to bring Scouts face to face with forest conservation management in a program known as The Boy Scout Forestry Camp. Writing later in the September 1935 issue of *The Forestry Chronicle*, he explained the program and how it started in 1929.

The ''Palace'': the Richardson's camp tent home.

"The camp was the idea of a few leaders of the Scout movement (himself included) to give Scouts an opportunity to do some practical work in forestry. . . The programme focused on reforestation as the most significant activity."

The spring planting period was selected because it tied into the planting season of the Forestry Branch. The Lands and Forests' Angus Station was chosen as the camp location.

At the end of the camp, each participant received a Forestry Camp Toggle made up of three wooden beads strung on a lace of buckskin. One bead was made from white pine to represent the importance of this species to lumber in Ontario. The second bead was made from spruce in recognition of its importance to the pulp and paper industry; and the third bead was made from Jack Pine to denote the importance of this species in natural reforestation (particularly after fires) and to symbolize the recovery of wasted forest and agriculture lands through reforestation. The buckskin lace represented the wildlife of the forest.

From a very basic forest conservation program in 1924 until 1991, it is estimated that Scouts, Guides, Cubs, and Brownies in Ontario have planted 60 million trees on 45,000 thousand acres (18,200 ha) of treeless land.

RICHARDSON'S STRATEGY

The Scouting Association realized through Richardson's influence significant benefits in economic funding under the guise of educational, technical, and administrative services. On the Forestry Branch side, Richardson knew that he was building good-will and public awareness of his government's involvement

*Kekedowigamig at the Blue
Spring Scout Reserve*

with this well-respected youth organization. The pay-off would be a more informed and sympathetic public for the government's conservation management programs.

Using his influence and administration skill, Richardson arranged in 1930 for the Forestry Branch to present a rustic pavilion called "The Kekedowigamig" (Meeting Place) to the Ebor Park-Gilwell camp. For the presentation ceremony, the testimonial text read in part, "in recognition of the services by Scouting in promoting reforestation in Ontario".

Within a year, again acting as a member of the development committee for Ebor Park, Richardson and the Forestry Branch along with some prominent Scouters provided the know-how and funds for the construction of another building, "The Caravansary".

THE ONTARIO EXECUTIVE ROLE

Richardson was appointed to the Ontario Executive Committee in 1932. This was the year that he arranged for the preparation of a mimeograph booklet for Boy Scouts (Ontario) attending the Angus Forestry Camps and trying for a Forester Badge. This excellent primer in Forest Management included identification of 28 native tree species and 17 native shrubs; discussion on the products of the forest, harvesting and manufacturing; kinds and effects of forest fires; government forestry organizations and activities, that included reforestation; and discussion on forest insects and fungi.

In 1934, Richardson met a senior Scouter-in-training, John Atkinson, who was to be closely associated with Arthur Herbert in later years. Atkinson was attending a leadership course at the Ebor Camp and Richardson was one of the instructors. Within a year, Richardson's value to Scouting was significantly recognized when the Association appointed him Vice-President of the Ontario Executive Committee, an office he held until 1943. The camp was named the Blue Spring Scout Reserve.

BLUE SPRING CAMP

The Ontario Council by 1936 decided to find a new and permanent location for its leadership camp. For this, a search committee under the chairmanship of Richardson was set up. An ideal location was found not far from Acton; well-treed, with the beautiful sparkling clear Eramosa River running through the property.

Again with Richardson's initiative, a log structure was erected at the gate of the camp. The dining hall fireplace of the new "Kekedowigamig" followed the original design and featured a prominent stone from the original fireplace.

Kekedowigamig at Blue Spring Scout Reserve — lounge fireplace with stone in mantel from the original at Ebor Park

MEDAL OF MERIT

Richardson was to remain as chairman of the development committee of Blue Spring Camp for the next 30 years. His drive and determination on improving the property was so effective that Blue Spring became known in Canada as an excellent Scout training camp. As a testimony to this and his leadership in teaching and developing the Scouts Forestry programs, the Boy Scout Association of Canada awarded him in February 1937 the Medal Of Merit — "In recognition of outstanding work for the Scout Movement during a period of seven years' service." The presentation was made by the then Governor General and Chief Scout for Canada, Rt. Hon. Lord Tweedsmuir.

That year, Richardson became a member of the Canadian General Council and the following year he was made Vice-President of the Ontario Provincial Council.

From 1939 and for the war years, many of the Scouting programs were involved with the War effort and the Forestry camps were suspended. It was in April of 1944, after his discharge from the army, that John Atkinson returned to Scouting as Field Director in charge of Blue Spring Camp. With encouragement from Richardson, Atkinson re-activated the Forestry Camp program in 1947 working with the supervisor in charge of the Midhurst/Angus, Simcoe County operation of the Department of Lands and Forests. Atkinson, referring to the millions of trees planted at Canadian Forces Base (CFB), Camp Borden were put there by Boy Scouts. "The armoured corps," Atkinson reflected, "in subsequent years knocked many of the trees down as they demonstrated to tank-training recruits the capabilities of tanks."

THE FIRE!

Atkinson remembers Richardson as a hard driver,

"He had certain ideas and he wanted them carried out his way. Also, he had the habit of appearing when least expected."

These characteristics were reflected in accounts by others who worked under Richardson. Atkinson laughingly recalled an incident that took place at Blue Spring Camp,

"I remember getting hell from Arthur Herbert. It was July and we were trimming cedar trees. We had a good fire going for burning the trimmings near the Kekedowigamig building. When he saw what we were up to, he lit into me for having the fire, pointing out how big it was. I protested that it wasn't that big or even dangerous. It was under control and we had shovels, rakes, and a water pump nearby. We were a 100 feet [30 m] from the building and nowhere near where they would do some harm. But Arthur Herbert persisted and scolded, 'Do you realize that nothing will ever grow on that soil where you are burning! You will have sterilized the soil!' I knew enough not to argue with him, he was my boss. Now, every time I burn refuse outside at my cottage, I think of Arthur Herbert. Up there I now use a steel drum."

Gates of Blue Spring Scout Reserve

MORE AWARDS, MORE HONOURS!

In the last year of the war, 1945, Richardson was elected President of the Ontario Provincial Council and within the year appointed to the Executive Committee for the Canadian General Council.

A.H. Richardson as President of the Ontario Scout Council, 1945-1951

The Silver Acorn

In a letter of January 20, 1949 from the Deputy Chief Executive Commissioner, W.L. Currier, in Ottawa to W.H.J. (Jaff) Tisdale, Ontario's Provincial Commissioner, he recommended the awarding of the Distinguished Service medal, The Silver Acorn. The award was made "For especially Distinguished Service to Scouting".

At the end 1951 Arthur Herbert retired as President of the Ontario Council and was appointed Honourary Vice-President where he continued to play an active part on the Executive Committee.

CAs HELP AGAIN!

By 1955, Richardson had convinced the Humber Valley, Grand Valley, Upper Thames River, and Don Valley Conservation Authorities to underwrite the cost of publishing the "Forester Badge" booklet in a professionally designed form. The production and editing of the book was carried out by Richardson's able assistant, A. (Alf) S.L. Barnes.

A year later, again using his influence with the Minister of Planning and Development and the funding from 15 Conservation Authorities he published a booklet outlining the requirements for four new proficiency Scouts Conservation Badges — Soil, Water, Forest, and Wildlife. Again, Alf Barnes was the author. The book's use spread to Scout troops in other provinces, especially the following year when a National Conservation theme, reflecting Richardson's influence was promoted by Scouting.

THE SILVER WOLF

The final honour from scouting to Arthur Herbert took place in the awards announced from Government House, Ottawa on July 1st, 1958 by the Chief Scout of Canada and the first Canadian-born Governor General, the Right Honourable Vincent Massey. Richardson had been awarded the highest recognition of national importance for service of the most exceptional character to Scouting, the Silver Wolf medal. In his letter written the previous April to Jackson Dodds,

CBE, Deputy Chief Scout, citing Arthur Herbert for the award, the Provincial Commissioner for Ontario, Frank A. Worth, advocated:

"Scouting owes a great debt of gratitude to Mr. Richardson not only for his personal interest in our work, but also for the interest and assistance he has been able to propagate with the influential people in both Government and private circles. . . . Mr. Richardson has over the past years been tireless in his efforts to promote leadership training."

*Covers of Scouting handbooks
by A.H. Richardson*

Chapter 5 The Conservation Saga

In the early decades of the 20th century, the concern about the expanding areas of denuded and wasted lands brought forth the call for reforestation. Advocates for reforestation at that time included the Canadian Forestry Association, the Canadian Society of Forest Engineers, and several prominent Canadians on the national scene. In the 1910 period in Ontario, the concern was brought to the attention of the government and the public by the Fruit Grower's Association of Ontario and the Ontario Agricultural and Experimental Union. Among the individuals pioneering reforestation in the province, there was one who was to gain considerable prominence as history proved. A native son of Ridgeway, Ontario, Edmond J. Zavitz, was to be later identified as the ''father of reforestation''.

ZAVITZ!

Ed Zavitz preceded Richardson by ten years as a graduate from McMaster University. His interest in forestry had been sparked after attending a meeting of the Canadian Forestry Association held in Toronto on an evening in 1902. There he met Thomas Southworth, the manager of the Brockville *Recorder* and, at that time, Director of Ontario's Bureau of Forestry, and an associate, Judson Clark, the first university-trained forester (Cornell) to be hired by the Bureau.

In the summer of 1904, Zavitz took a job at Guelph's Ontario Agricultural College (OAC) and set up a small tree nursery using planting stock from the United States. The idea of a forest agriculture program

Ed Zavitz

at OAC had been encouraged by two agricultural groups, the Fruit Growers' Association and the Ontario Agricultural and Experimental Union. That fall, Ed Zavitz enrolled at Michigan University and graduated in the spring of 1905 with a Master in Silviculture degree.

In the fall of that year, Zavitz was appointed to the staff of the Ontario Agricultural College with a job description that included three major tasks: first, to lecture on farm forestry; second, to produce nursery stock suitable for forest planting; and finally, to carry out extension work with land owners (mainly farmers). The OAC nursery program became a co-operative one with farm groups. That same year the Ministry of Agriculture chose Zavitz to carry out a survey of a number of southern Ontario counties to report on the extent of the area and damage caused by sand-blown wasteland that was previously for-ested lands. This alarming situation had resulted from unchecked exploitation by lumber operators, and lands cleared and later abandoned by farmers due to poor farming practices and submarginal soil conditions. The survey completed, Zavitz, now a professor at OAC, submitted his findings in a 1908 document entitled "Report on the Reforestation of Waste Lands in Southern Ontario". The document aroused serious interest and support from farmers and officials in the county and provincial governments.

In 1911, three years after his report, the provincial government passed the Counties Reforestation Act. Action on the Act was interrupted by the 1914-18 War. However, in 1919, the provincial government, with E.C. Drury now Premier, reactivated the pro-gram under Zavitz's direction. By 1921, a Provincial Reforestation Act was passed.

THE FIERY INFERNOS OF 1911 AND 1916

In November of 1912, Zavitz left OAC to take the post as the Director of Forestry in the Department of Lands and Forests. With his new responsibilities he gave up his lecture series at OAC and the course became a job for a part-time lecturer. Zavitz's major

Southern Ontario wastelands mapped by Ed Zavitz

role in his new job was to supervise fire protection for the railways of the province. The previous year, the populace had witnessed a wildfire holocaust that engulfed Timmins, South Porcupine, Porquis Junction, and Cochrane, killing 73 people and devastating a half million acres (100 000 ha) of forests. ''We are in need of a province-wide permanent fire protection service,'' Zavitz insisted. Before this new service could be set up, catastrophe struck again in 1916. Numerous small fires broke out.

Fanned by violent winds, the fires joined into a raging inferno that raced along the Timiskaming and Northern Ontario Railway to the Abitibi River, ravaging an area equivalent to 20 townships or 1329 square miles (3442 km²) of forested land, destroying seven towns, including Matheson, part of Iroquois Falls and Cochrane, and culminating in the deaths of 224 people. Intensified public demand provoked the Government into action to overhaul the protection system. The Minister of Lands and Forests, Howard Ferguson, summoned Zavitz to his office and instructed him to reorganize the service. By the next year, 1917, the Forest Fire and Prevention Act was passed, with Zavitz appointed the Provincial Forester to administer the Act.

In the 1919 elections, the United Farmers of Ontario Party took over under the leadership of E.C. Drury. Zavitz's good fortune continued as Drury was a long-time friend.

RICHARDSON HIRED BY LANDS AND FORESTS

The new fire protection service opened opportunities for more jobs. Zavitz believed that the Department needed more professionally educated men in Forestry. With few exceptions, the University of Toronto's Faculty of Forestry was the main source. One of the exceptions appeared at Zavitz's office in the fall of 1920, Arthur Herbert Richardson. Fresh from Harvard with a masters in Silviculture, Richardson was hired by Zavitz as ''Forester'' in the Forestry Branch. Richardson moved enthusiastically into the reforestation program in Southern Ontario.

COUNTY FORESTS EXPANDED

Although the Counties Reforestation Act of 1911 permitted the province and any county to co-operate in establishing large forest tracts as well as supplying tree stock free for private lands, the program got sparse action until after the War. The growing demand for native seed and the need for better economics in providing seeds for planting brought about the establishment of the Angus Seed Extraction plant. Constructed under Richardson's supervision, it was ready for business by 1924. The county reforestation program occupied much of Richardson's time. Meanwhile the seed collection program under George Bayly and the extraction program supervised by Ralph Carmen only required cursory attention by Richardson.

To encourage the reforestation of wasted lands, the early programs were initiated to demonstrate the methods and advantages of reforesting.

RICHARDSON THE WRITER

Arthur Herbert was a skilled communicator when it came to building public awareness of forestry and forestry matters. He had the ability to write well, as evidenced when one reviews the number of Forestry Branch publications that bore his name, reads his articles and scientific papers, and follows his parallel ''career'' as editor/secretary of the national forestry publication, *The Forestry Chronicle*.

One of his earliest efforts for the Forestry Branch was a 71-page booklet, ''Forest Tree Planting''. This 1924 instructional guide on planting trees was an aid to farmers and private landholders. The same year he wrote a companion edition of ''Forest Trees for Distribution'' and updated it again in 1926. In a 1927 booklet, ''The Woodlot'', he encouraged farmers to apply the silvicultural technique of sustained management, controlled cutting, and protection from their grazing livestock. Within a year four more booklets under his editorship were being distributed by the Forestry Branch: ''Windbreaks and Shelter Belts'', ''Tree Planting Acts of Ontario'', ''Gathering Pine Cones and Other Seeds'', and ''The Municipal Forest''.

Pamplets by A.H. Richardson

RICHARDSON THE TEACHER

It was at this time that the part-time position of Forestry lecturer at OAC became vacant. Zavitz prevailed on Richardson to take on this job, a task that brought Arthur Herbert to Guelph and OAC for two days a week over the next 16 years. Ken Higgs, former General Manager of the Metro Toronto and Region Conservation Authority, recalled, ''As a first-year university forestry student in 1948 working on the Don Valley survey, I met Mr. Richardson. He was a capable teacher, although I think publishing was his preference.''

As we have learned, Richardson used his teaching skills in the Boy Scout programs, starting in 1929. John Atkinson recollects,

''As a leader on our training courses, Mr. Richardson as an instructor was well liked and well accepted. He had an excellent (teaching) method for demonstrating tree identification.''

RICHARDSON TAKES CHARGE OF REFORESTATION

The Forestry Branch was now an established entity in the Ministry, with reforestation, fire protection, and survey functioning effectively. Reforestation was the area most recognized by the public. With this in mind, Premier Howard Ferguson appointed Zavitz in 1926 to the new post of Deputy Minister of Forestry. The following year, Richardson was appointed Forester in Charge of Reforestation.

Before the end of the decade, Richardson's writing skills were used to describe the status of forestry in Ontario. The booklet ''Forestry in Ontario'' covered the Department's growth and development in fire protection, air operations, reforestation, and surveys.

DISASTER STRIKES ONTARIO FORESTRY BRANCH

In the spring of 1935, disaster befell the Ontario Forestry Branch with drastic staff reductions. The newly elected Liberal government instituted severe cutbacks and replacements. One hundred and thirteen employees including many foresters, with

Unemployed march in Calgary in 1935

service records from 1 to 23 years, were fired. Some replacements to the forestry service were "unqualified political appointees" such as a non-technical and inexperienced Deputy Minister. The Canadian Society of Forest Engineers mounted pressure on the Ontario government to take such action as would ensure the continued proper management of Ontario's forest resources. A similar hatchet process was being carried out by the Federal government under Prime Minister R.B. Bennett spurred on by country-wide pressures to economize.

From the pages of *The Forestry Chronicle*, Richardson called for the use of effective communication to educate public opinion on what is good forest management practice.

"An informed and aroused public will be strong enough to influence the politicians and force the property owner (government and private) to handle the areas properly. We have been too timid because we were not convinced that real forestry paid off from every angle. We have gone whole heartedly for fire protection, improved logging, and converting methods, but we have shied off when it comes to silviculture. A silviculturalist is looked upon as an extremist. The consequence of all this is that we (professional foresters) have not occupied a place in the public esteem that we are entitled to. We are a worthy profession and should not hesitate to impress this fact upon the general public."

In a later editorial, Richardson stated,

"The responsibility for the care and protection of Canada's forests, their proper use and conservation rests directly on the shoulders of the forestry profession. Forests are a necessity to our agriculturalist, our water power, the mining industries, and the people at large for the best kind of recreation. Forests can only be properly handled by foresters."

FOR THE PEOPLE, BY THE PEOPLE

Example of planting for future forest growth

Public interest in the natural history of Ontario in 1930 was primarily a domain of some professional scientists and amateur naturalists with an eager curiosity in nature. With this common interest, it wasn't long before they formed themselves into nature clubs. In early 1931, motivated by a senior group, the Brodie Club of Toronto, an organizing committee was formed to examine the possibility of forming a provincial organization. On May 15, 1931 in University of Toronto's Hart House, the Federation of Ontario Naturalists (FON) was chartered. It was composed of clubs from Chatham, London, Hamilton, Kingston, and Toronto. One of the new Federation's notable contributions to the conservation movement took place in the 1937-38 period with the initiating of a survey of the natural resources of King Township. The prime value of this survey conducted and reported on by Ken Mayall, later an associate of Richardson, was a conclusion subscribed to by Richardson,

".. . that conservation cannot be attained by piecemeal methods, but rather that it must be accompanied with a multi-purpose program for the renewal of all the natural resources in an area."

The alarming growth of resource depletion caused by needless deforestation and the deterioration of wasted and abandoned farm lands into desertlike conditions had triggered concern by some prominent individuals and organizations in Southern Ontario. They included amiable Watson H. Porter, managing editor of *The Farmer's Advocate* magazine; the well-regarded Monroe Landon, farmer, naturalist, and conservationist; and from the University of Western Ontario's Department of Applied Biology, Professor J.D. Detwiler. They, along with the Norfolk Chamber of Commerce, had been calling for concerted action by individuals and groups with a genuine concern for conservation, flood control, and reforestation.

In the September issue of *The Farmer's Advocate*, Porter wrote an article entitled "A New Reforestation Policy for Ontario". A series of meetings was held in London, Guelph, and Bowmanville with representatives from counties of the surrounding areas, particularly members of the agricultural and reforestation committees. As a result, the Ontario Conservation and Reforestation Association (OCRA) was formed in January 1937. Richardson acted on the provincial committee as the representative of the Forestry Branch, Ministry of Lands and Forests.

AWAKENING PUBLIC INTEREST . . . TOURS

Richardson had exceptional skills of how to market and communicate the conservation message to the people of the province. Starting in 1937 and into 1941, he, along with committee representation from OCRA, the counties concerned, and the Department of Agriculture, organized across Southern Ontario a series of well-planned Conservation Tours. Richardson explained,

"The tours usually took a whole day and in many cases included an itinerary of more than one hundred miles [160 km]. Such a tour included inspection of reforestation projects, farm planning, pollution, water problems, and woodlot management."

Sometimes a Minister or Deputy Minister would participate. Richardson felt it was important to bring the Government VIPs to the People.

THE GUELPH CONFERENCE

In Toronto at its 1941 annual meeting, the OCRA members were concerning themselves with the possibility of using the returned veterans as the needed workers in the post-war conservation programs. It was assumed by many that a serious economic recession would be the result of closing down wartime industries. A committee that included Richardson was appointed to study the setting up of a Canadian conservation corps and other plans related to conservation and reforestation.

Preliminary inquiry revealed that the Federation of Ontario Naturalists had also appointed a committee to develop a similar plan. Acting in unison, a meeting was called for April 25th at the Ontario College of

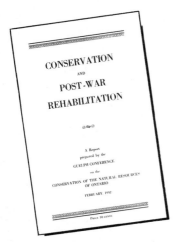

Pamphlet: Conservation and
Post-War Rehabilitation 1942

Agriculture, Guelph. The event was named the
Guelph Conference and J.D. Thomas of the National
Selective Service, Ottawa was elected chairman.

The report of the Conference was published in a
booklet "Conservation and Post-War Rehabilitation"
written by Professor A.F. Coventry, an esteemed biologist from the University of Toronto and a leading
activist in FON. Approving the report were The
Ontario Conservation and Reforestation Association;
The Federation of Ontario Naturalists; The Canadian
Society of Forest Engineers, Southern Ontario
Section; The Royal Canadian Institute; Canadian
Society of Technical Agriculturalists; and the Ontario
Federation of Anglers and Hunters. Other organizations sent representatives. An examination of the
membership roster of four of the attending organiza-
tions would have found the name of A.H. Richardson
listed.

THE CONFERENCE REPORT

The disturbing frankness of the report pinpointed the
unhealthy state of the renewable natural resources
particularly in Old Ontario (the long-settled, highly
populated, agricultural areas of Southern Ontario).
Conclusions from the Conference listed the serious-
ness of the following depletions: soil had become
impoverished through loss of fertility; water sources
were drying up — 80% of the streams that flowed a
hundred years ago were now temporarily dry during
the year; the quality of water in the receiving lakes
and rivers had lessened through ill-advised drainage
of swamps; what waters remained were largely pol-
luted by industrial waste and sewage waste from
municipalities of all sizes; forest covers had danger-
ously decreased; erosion by wind and water was on
the increase; and the impact of all this was damaging
fish and wildlife habitat and population.

The remedial action needed as described by
Richardson was "replacing the unplanned, individ-
ualistic exploitation of the past hundred years by
planned management, based on knowledge and
recognizing public as well as private interest."

Guelph Conference (1941)
Monument dedication

RICHARDSON APPOINTED CHAIRMAN

The rehabilitation of the returning veterans into useful employment was being considered by many municipalities and groups across Canada. In the leadership role, the federal government appointed an Advisory Committee on Reconstruction with Dr. F. Cyril James, principal of McGill University, as its chairman. A sub-committee on Conservation and Development of Natural Resources headed by Dr. R.C. Wallace, principal of Queen's University, was set up to present a policy and program towards full development of Canada's natural resources and how the recommended programs could aid in providing employment opportunities at war's end. In August, a committee from the Guelph Conference led by its chairman, J.D. Thomas, travelled to Ottawa to meet with the Committee on Reconstruction to outline the Guelph Conference, and how it would fit into the federal government's veterans rehabilitation program. The committee found the federal government ready to co-operate with Ontario and share the costs for a demonstration survey as a special piece of conservation research that could be generally applied to Canada. Returning to Toronto, Thomas discussed the proposal with the Premier, Mitchell Hepburn, who gave his support and passed its implementation to his Minister of Lands and Forests, N.O. Hipel.

Honourable J.R. Simonett, Minister of Energy and Resource Management, and A.H. Richardson at inauguration of the Ganaraska Region Conservation Authority

Hipel authorized the appointment of the Inter-departmental Committee on Conservation and Rehabilitation with Richardson as its full-time chairman. The chosen watershed to be surveyed was the 103-square-mile (2590 ha) Ganaraska River drainage area, with its outlet into Lake Ontario at Port Hope. On June 15, 1943 the Minister of Lands and Forests received the 450-page report authored by Richardson. Of the compliments that were expressed about the report, Richardson "cherished most" that of Dana Porter, MPP Toronto-St. George. "He held the report high in his hand and announced, 'Mr. Richardson, this is a classic!. . .'" The mutual esteem between Porter and Richardson was to soon prove advantageous for Arthur Herbert's career. A prophetic analysis of the report came from Professor J.R. Dymond of U. of T. who had been secretary-treasurer of the Guelph Conference. He commented,

". . . the survey of the Ganaraska River basin and its recommendations . . . have recently been published in a report which may well become a landmark in Ontario conservation literature."

LANDS AND FORESTS REORGANIZED

While those concerned with the Conservation movement were busy arousing public interest in 1941, the Department of Lands and Forests was about to embark on a metamorphosis in its organization, starting with the appointment of a new Minister, N.O. Hipel. In very short order, under advisement, Hipel selected as his Deputy Minister, Frank A. MacDougall. MacDougall was the first graduate forester to reach this position. Possessing a terse, direct manner, the well-qualified MacDougall had earned his spurs in the successful establishment of the Kirkwood Forest Management Unit near Thessalon in Northern Ontario; but more important, as Superintendent of Algonquin Park, the most senior position in the Department, MacDougall had prepared himself well and knew where he wanted to take the Ministry in the future.

The Forestry Branch was the genesis of the reorganized Department, having set up over the years an effective forest protection system, created a district

Trucks used for conservation work

administrative organization, developed and broadened the reforestation system, and implemented the forest management principles under professional foresters. Designated to become part of the Timber Management Division, the Forestry Branch transition was postponed for the time being because of the presence of E.J. Zavitz, then 66. Zavitz showed no desire to retire nor to assume the control of the Timber Management Division. It was feared that any change in Zavitz's personal status and his intimate identification with the successful reforestation program might arouse public resentment. For the time being the division was identified as the Reforestation and Conservation Division until Zavitz retired in 1953. Its role was to carry out reforestation in Southern Ontario, operate the provincial forest nurseries, and perform extension services to land owners.

RICHARDSON AND THE ENIGMA

One would have expected that the organizational chart, appearing in the Ministry's 1941 Annual Report and listing the names of key personnel, would have included A.H. Richardson. Such was not the case. The competition for the senior positions was intense but apparently Richardson's career in Lands and Forests had become limited. It appeared that he had run afoul of some of his associates and superiors in the Ministry whose influence put him into a situation of having a job but no position. His assertive style, his ability to recognize and meld others' ideas with his own, his communication skills, and political acumen, apparently disturbed some of his associates. Whether their concerns were deflected to the attention of Deputy Minister MacDougall or whether MacDougall himself had personal misgivings are areas of speculation. However, MacDougall would have had the final say in the matter.

Richardson's high profile in the conservation movement provided a solution to the situation, and as events proved, a launching pad to a new status. It was at this time that Richardson was busily involved with the Ontario Conservation and Reforestation Association.

On the surface, Richardson's role in the Department appeared to be as a representative for special assignments. One example was his appointment as Chairman of the Interdepartmental Committee for Conservation and Rehabilitation followed by the appointment to direct the Ganaraska survey project. His high profile arising out of this survey, for which he was awarded a Forestry Engineering degree from U. of T. probably exacerbated the relationship with his Lands and Forests peers.

RICHARDSON TRANSFERS TO A NEW MINISTRY

In 1944, Premier George Drew set up a new ministry, that of Planning and Development, to deal with future plans of the government in anticipation of the post-war era. One of the major branches in the new Ministry was Conservation. Just why this section of activity was not set up in Lands and Forests is puzzling, as it must have disturbed the senior Ministry and the MacDougall domain. (It wasn't until 1962, the year Richardson retired, that the Branch returned to Lands and Forests, as the Conservation Authorities Branch.) A former deputy minister expressed his opinion in this way,

"Richardson was well connected politically. He sold the idea of Conservation in (Ministry) Planning and Development to Dana Porter."

Certainly the pressure for more action on Conservation in all forms crossed ministerial lines that included agriculture, forestry, mining, tourism, and public works.

In May 1944, at a conference in Toronto, Drew named Dana Porter as Minister for Planning and Development, following which Professor George B. Langford, Professor of Mining Geology of U. of T., was appointed Director. At that time in the bureaucratic order, a director was senior to a Deputy Minister and in this arrangement it put the incumbent in a favorable position to co-ordinate the work with other departments.

By the fall, Dana Porter decided to hold a conference in London to examine the needs and a new approach to conservation. The theme of the conference was "River Valley Development in Southern Ontario". Richardson was seconded from Lands and Forests by the new ministry to help organize the meeting. Dr. J.D. Detwiler, Professor of Applied Biology, U. of Western Ontario, and President of the Canadian Conservation Association, was named chairman. Noted members of the conservation movement from governments (municipal and provincial), educators, and conservation-oriented organizations attended. At the Saturday luncheon, the Minister of Lands and Forests, W.G. Thompson, officially released the Ganaraska Report.

The resolution committee, in a key recommendation, set the stage for the future with this resolution.

". . . that the government of Ontario be urged to establish a conservation authority for Ontario responsible to the government, having as its principal function the bringing about of co-ordination and co-operation amongst all agencies in Ontario, carrying out and promoting conservation projects with the object of formulating and putting into effect a unified program for the rehabilitation and wise use of all our renewable natural resources."

RICHARDSON NAMED CHIEF CONSERVATION ENGINEER

The formation of a Conservation Branch was agreed upon and Richardson was asked to become its head as Chief Conservation Engineer. The transfer was made in November 1944. Within days, Richardson with some members of the Ganaraska Advisory Board and a county engineer from the Upper Thames Valley visited the Muskingum Watershed Conservancy in Ohio. This successfully operating conservation area and the Grand Valley Conservation Commission program were to be the pattern projects. The first order of business was to write the Bill for the 1945 Legislature which would become the Conservation Authorities Act. Identified as Bill 81, it was opposed by the Co-operative Commonwealth Federation (CCF) which was anything but co-operative as political haggling stopped the Bill from reaching the floor before the legislature was dissolved.

Upper Thames Conservation Authority crest (1953) designed by A.H. Richardson

Alf S. Barnes

*Professor G. Ross Lord —
consultant to Ganaraska
Region Conservation
Authority in hydraulic
engineering*

THE EARLY STAFF

Meanwhile Richardson was settling the new Conservation Branch for business in a large house at 15 Queen's Park Crescent near the east block of the Parliament Buildings. During a spirited debate in Parliament, the CCF leader accused Premier George Drew of operating a secret arm of the Provincial Police from the House. It was quickly dubbed the "Gestapo Building".

Richardson had gathered together a small but efficient technical staff that would establish the numerous Authorities that were to follow. For the forestry work, Richardson knew immediately who he wanted, in the person of A.S.L. (Alf) Barnes. Barnes had worked for Richardson in the 1930s in seed extraction work at Angus directed by its supervisor, R.S. Carmen. Reports on Barnes must have impressed Richardson, for when they met in Ottawa in 1941 (Barnes was in the armed forces and Richardson was launching the Ganaraska Survey), he commented to Barnes, "I wish I could get you out of the army, Alf, to work on the Ganaraska survey." Twenty-one years later Barnes succeeded his long-time associate as head of the Branch. Other "originals" were Leslie Laking who took care of land use; Harry Christian, the accountant who managed the office and supplies and the general business of the Branch; Clayton Bush for engineering; Verschoyle Blake did the history research; and Professor G. Ross Lord from the University of Toronto, who served as consultant in hydraulic engineering.

A little later, others were added, including John Murray, an hydraulic engineer who directed the field work in that sphere; Ken Mayall, who had made his mark with his report on the King Township survey, took charge of the wildlife and recreation section; while Herb F. Crown handled extension work; and Professor F.D. Ide of U. of T. was the consultant in fish culture.

RICHARDSON DIRECTS THE UPPER THAMES SURVEY

Since 1937, the annual flood situation in the Thames River Valley had been an ongoing problem with no tangible action resulting. Pressure had mounted to such a pitch that, in spite of the delay in passing Bill 81, Dana Porter decided to approve the Upper Thames survey. Richardson, acting in his new capacity, directed the project, and prepared the report.

Meanwhile, coincident with this event was consideration of Bill 81. The Conservation Authorities Act was back before the Legislature in 1946 and was passed. A steering committee headed by Watson Porter lost no time in pressing for the formation of an Authority and, after wide debate, the Upper Thames River Conservation Authority was created on September 18, 1947. (That year, Richardson added to his professional résumé by being certified as a registered member of the Ontario Professional Engineers Association.) This Authority held a special appeal for Richardson over the years and his mark was registered in its operation for 13 years. He was its first Chief Officer until 1960. In 1953, he applied his graphic talent by designing the Authority's crest with the Latin inscription, *"conservatio ab populo"* (Conservation by the People).

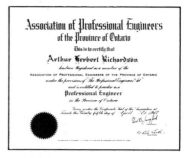

Association of Professional Engineers certificate awarded to A.H. Richardson in 1947

RICHARDSON THE PUBLIC RELATIONS TACTICIAN

It could have been a characteristic acquired from his father, Samuel, that gave Richardson a natural talent in the skills of a publicist, and in a broader sense, a public relations practitioner. He knew the subject of his message, conservation and forest management, better than any public relations officer ever would. Richardson realized that entertainment was a strong communication tool in educating the masses. He also knew that, in selling the public an idea, you must spend significant time on selling your superiors on the advantages of the idea well before you turn your attention to the public. For this, Richardson developed reliable rapport with the politicians and the fallout of that relationship was that credit for a successful program was focused on him. This was a normal result; after all he was the "Chief".

Richardson was astute enough to work behind the scenes and put the political person up front. His

PROGRAMME
DE
L'EXCURSION
NISEE PAR
S DE PRESCOTT ET DE
CCASION DE LEUR
RNEE
ISEMENT

PROGRAMME
AND
TOUR

PRESCOTT & RUSSELL COUNTIES
Forestry Field Day

PTEMBRE

arbren de ces
t me cache à la
entre en moi-
i m'écoute et
'GO)

SEPTEMBER FIRST
1938

Programs in English and French editions for a Forestry Field Day in September 1938

Mrs. A.H. Richardson and Herbert in the costume of Phineas Peabody at the opening of Black Creek Pioneer Village, June 1960

most effective skill was in relating to the politicians. He realized they needed events to bring them to the people and he needed them to bring the people to the events.

Richardson used several forms of the printed message: magazines, booklets, flyers, posters, photography, news releases, articles, and stories. He recognized the appeal of the use of children in sending any message to the people. In his public events, such as Field Days, there were always school children or Scouts and Guides carrying out an activity, such as planting trees or performing a pageant.

Richardson's attention to detail was always important in organizing events. Even language and culture were noted. For a 1938 Field Day held in the Prescott & Russell counties of the Ottawa Valley, the poster and program were printed separately in French and English.

His sense of theatrics and musical talent were used on more than one occasion. In 1940, for a conservation picnic at the Sand Banks and Vivian Conservation areas, he wrote the lyrics for a song entitled, "Hail, Hail, Conservation", set to the tune of "My Hero", from the operatta *The Chocolate Soldier*. He then persuaded three of his committee members to join him as a quartet and sang it to the cheering crowd. In 1960 at Metro Toronto's Black Creek Pioneer Village dedication, Richardson garbed in top hat and frock coat took the part of Phineas Peabody, the first reeve of the Village and strolled the streets greeting visitors and residents alike.

OUR VALLEY

If there was one memorial to Richardson it was the periodical magazine *Our Valley*. First published as a mimeographed newsletter in March 1952, it was upgraded in 1955 to a glossy booklet published twice a year. Its message was separated into several sections with each section featuring a report on activities and development in a specific Conservation Authority. With Richardson as editor, his Toronto staff was the production crew.

One curious side note about *Our Valley* was the philosophic commentaries and verses that appeared from time to time written by Samuel Woodstock. The quaintness of these inserts was carried out in the design of each issue even to the point of using period-style typography. On the back cover of the first issue, S. Woodstock wrote, in archaic English,

"My son, I admonifh you to cherifh the little waters, for thefe replenifh the mighty rivers which nourifh our thirfty land."

In a 1958 issue was this message by Woodstock,

"Conservation with its abundance of good things, is rooted in the future."

Samuel Woodstock was of course the invention of Richardson. The interpretation of the name has some interest. "Samuel" was the name of his Baptist father and "Woodstock" was the town where the Baptist college, The Christian Literary Institute, was founded and later amalgamated with the Toronto Baptist College to become McMaster University, Richardson's alma mater.

Our Valley ceased publishing in 1961. According to Ken Higgs,

". . . (this) beautiful report ended very abruptly because somebody in the legislature criticized (Premier) Leslie Frost for the glossy and expensive publications *Sylva* and *Our Valley*. From the floor of the legislature, Frost cancelled both publications."

In 1954, the Department of Lands and Forests created a Division to administer parks. By 1956 a Parks Integration Board was set up to approve the establishment of new park areas as recommended by an advisory committee. The Minister of Planning and Development was a member of the Board, and Richardson was named to the Advisory committee.

THE AUTHORITIES IN THE RICHARDSON YEARS

Each conservation survey had a set pattern with few exceptions. The summer program was prepared and directed by the technical staff from the Toronto office. Field work was then laid out for the various sections: forestry, wildlife and recreation, land use, and

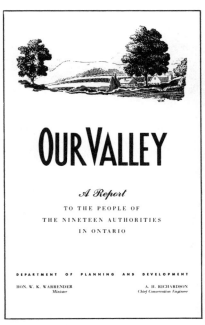

Title page of Our Valley

hydraulics. Under direction and supervision, some 40 or more students, mostly from university, would go about gathering the required information. Some time during the work period, a press day for the local media was held so that they could view and see demonstrations of applied techniques for areas suitable for conservation activities. Later on, a tour would be held for members of the authority and municipal council within the targeted authority. At the presentation of the final report, a public meeting would be held that included displays using maps, photos, and charts.

Through the 16 years, Richardson and the Conservation Branch participated in, and gave leadership to many advances in soil conservation, recreation development, wildlife management, stream improvements, major dam installations for flood control, outdoor education camps for students and others.

Starting in 1946 with the Ausable River and Etobicoke Conservation Authorities, 37 other Conservation Authorities would be put in place by the time Richardson retired. This did not incude their further enlargement, nor amalgamation of one authority with a neighbouring one, as in 1957 when the Don Valley, Humber Valley, Etobicoke-Mimico, Rouge River, Duffin Creek, Highland Creek, and Petticoat Creek were amalgamated to form the Metropolitan Toronto and Region Conservation Authority. For the first year of this major conservation authority Richardson was appointed chairman, by Order-in-Council of the Ontario government. At the first annual meeting in February 1958, Dr. G. Ross Lord was installed as chairman.

Crest of the Metropolitan Toronto Regional Conservation Authority

THE RICHARDSON STYLE

In our behaviour and relations with others as we strive towards our career goals, we tend to develop certain inter-personal characteristics as perceived by our superiors, peers, and subordinates as appealing and acceptable, or irritating and disturbing. Arthur Herbert was no exception to this very human experience. Hal G. Hook, one-time executive director in the Water Resources section, had worked under Richardson on several surveys that included the Don,

Upper Thames, the Saugeen, and the Grand, had this to say about Richardson's management style.

"A funny situation that I thought about many times. Under today's set up of administration it would have been very unlikely that he would have been able to do the things that he did. A sort of law unto himself. He reported to nobody but the Minister. He retained the aura of an autocratic figure. In the early times, he retained control when an Authority was formed until they could get organized and run it themselves. That was the way he did things. . . . He knew what he wanted to do. In truth, these Authorities needed a strong father figure to begin with. He was it!"

THE GREENWOOD EMBARRASSMENT

Now in his 68th year, it seemed probable that Richardson's name would one day be identified with a Conservation Area. By 1958, the MTRCA had assembled 300 acres (121 ha) of land that was being readied as a Conservation Area east of Toronto in the East Duffin Creek/Greenwood area. The residents of the locality were looking forward to its opening as the Greenwood Conservation Area. In preparation for the opening dedication planned for August 6, 1958, the MTRCA set up a sub-committee to arrange the event. In their deliberation and enthusiasm, the members decided to change the name from Green-wood and take the opportunity to honour Richardson by naming it the "A. H. Richardson Conservation Area". Without confirming this name change with the Authority's Advisory Committee, plans for programs, signage, announcement cards, and an engraved cigar humidor for presentation went forward. It was not long before residents of the Green-wood area learned of the name change and exercised a people-power-protest that converted into political pressure. The implication quickly dawned on the office of the Minister of Planning and Development, W. M. Nickle, from which reaction was swift. In the final hours before the dedication event, the order came that the name was to be the "Greenwood Con-servation Area." The embarrassment to Richardson was predictable. His staff was shocked. Several days after the event they presented Arthur Herbert with the engraved humidor bearing his name.

RICHARDSON BEACH AND RICHARDSON LOOKOUT

The opening of the Fanshawe Dam in London on September 18, 1953 marked the first flood-control dam to be built on a conservation area. To service the recreational interests of the people of London and area, a park dedicated to Dr. J. Cameron Wilson, the first chairman of the Upper Thames River Conservation Authority, was part of the development. Within the park confines and bordering Fanshawe Lake was an attractive beach named Richardson Beach.

Ten years later on July 8, 1964, the Dean's Hill Conservation Area was opened, and an observation platform located at the top of an 850-foot (259 m) drumlin (rounded hill) was dedicated to Arthur Herbert Richardson and named the Richardson Lookout. As Richardson, with Winnifred at his side, took in the spectacular panorama of the Ganaraska watershed where it all began, and absorbed the splendour of man's work in harmony with nature, he probably recited a favourite biblical proverb.

A.H. Richardson and J. Cameron Wilson with a painting of Richardson Beach at Fanshawe Park

> "Where there is no vision, the people perish!"
> *Biblio Hebraic* (Prpb. xxix, 18)

MR. CONSERVATION RETIRES!!

In the Wednesday, February 14, 1962 edition of the *Toronto Telegram*, a headline read "Mr. Conservation Retires And Leaves . . . 19,718 Square Miles of Parkland." (That would be 5 106 962 ha)

"Mr. Conservation is Arthur Herbert Richardson who retired after 41 years' service with the Provincial Government."

Herbert and Winifred Richardson late in life

In describing the achievements of Ontario's Chief Conservation Engineer, the story read in part,

"... monuments to his public service are spread throughout the province in the form of parks, playgrounds, swimming areas, flood control and reforestation projects, pioneer villages, and land use demonstrations... He is the man responsible for the province's 31 conservation authorities ... of which he had a hand in forming.

" 'Highlight of his career,' said Mr. Richardson, 'was the signing of a three-fold agreement including MTRCA, the Upper Thames, and the Grand Conservation Authorities with the Federal and Provincial Governments.' ... It provides for a $50 000 000 flood-control project over the next 10 years with financial assistance from both senior governments.

"... He humbly maintained that he just helped implement a 'people's movement' in conservation."

What could serve as a fitting epitaph to Conservation and the vision of Arthur Herbert Richardson, was written by his long-time friend and successor as Chairman of the Metropolitan Toronto Region Conservation Authority, Dr. G. Ross Lord. Written as part of the introduction to Arthur Herbert's own book, *Conservation For The People*, published two years after his death, Dr. Lord concluded:

"The work of conservation will never end. Perhaps most conservationists are men of whom the prophet Joel wrote: 'Your old men shall dream dreams, your young men shall see visions.' Perhaps conservationists will always be setting aside lands so that they will not be all absorbed by the throbbing life of urban expansion, so that always some lands will be retained as oases of peace for those who toil in the city, so that in the years to come these valleys may echo with the laughter of children, so that young people may witness the ever-recurring miracle of spring, and so that parents may enjoy the solace of nature for tired bodies and minds."

THE BLOOMING ENDS

"During his ten years of retirement, Dad wrote his book, *Conservation For The People*. He had a heart attack in 1967. Recovering, he finished the book in November of 1971 and made arrangements for pictures, maps, and design. He celebrated Christmas and on December 27th suffered a heart attack and died. The completion of the book seemed to be a signal that he had finished what he wanted to do in this life.

"Several years previously, Dad had transplanted some pink lady slippers from the cottage property to the side of the garage of our home on Willingdon Avenue and every year they bloomed. In the spring of 1972 there were no blooms!"

Cathy Richardson

Index

References

Conservation and Post-War Rehabilitation, February, 1942
   A Report prepared by the Guelph Conference on the Natural Resources of Ontario
A Report on the Ganaraska Watershed
   A.H. Richardson MA, SMSilv., FE, Chief Conservation Engineer, Department of Planning and Development, 1944. Published by the Ontario Department of Planning and Development
Fifty Years of Reforestation in Ontario
   E.J. Zavitz, BA, MSF, LD. Ontario Department of Lands and Forests, 1960. Outlines the forest management process in Ontario with comment dating from 1871 to 1960
Renewing Nature's Wealth — A Centennial History
   Richard S. Lambert with Paul Pross, 1967, Ontario Department of Lands and Forests. A Centennial History of the Public Management of Lands, Forest & Wildlife in Ontario, 1763-1967. Library of Congress Catalog Card Number 67-26095. Published by The Hunter Rose Company
Expanding Forestry Horizons
   K.G. Fenson. Canadian Institute of Forestry. Evergreen Press Limited, 1972, Vancouver, B.C. A History of the Canadian Institute of Forestry, 1908-1969.
Twenty-Five Years of Conservation on the Upper Thames Watershed, 1947-73
   Published by the Upper Thames River Conservation Authority; Printer: The B-H Press, Stratford, Ontario. History of the Authority. A.H. Richardson designed the Authority's crest and was its first officer for thirteen years, 1943-1960.

Conservation by the People
   Arthur Herbert Richardson; Edited by A.S.L. Barnes; Published by University of Toronto Press, 1974, ISBN 0-8020-3329-6, for the Conservation Authorities of Ontario. The History of the Conservation Movement in Ontario to 1970
Forestry and Forestry Education in a Developing Country — A Canadian Dilemma. J.W.B. Sisam, Faculty of Forestry, University of Toronto, 1982
Identification Guide to the Trees of Canada. Jean Lauriault. Pubished by National Museum of Natural Sciences and Fitzhenry & Whiteside, 1989
Native Trees of Canada, R.C. Hosie. Published by Fitzhenry & Whiteside, 1979

Illustration Credits

We gratefully acknowledge those who gave us permission to use pictures from their collections:
Ontario Ministry of Lands and Forests
Metropolitan Toronto and Region Conservation Authority
Cathy Richardson
Paul Masterson
Fitzhenry & Whiteside archives

BUG BOOKS

Daddy Longlegs

Catherine Anderson

Heinemann Library
Chicago, IL

© 2003, 2008 Heinemann Library
a division of Reed Elsevier Inc.
Chicago, Illinois

Customer Service 888-454-2279
Visit our website at www.heinemannlibrary.com

Design: Kimberly R. Miracle and Cavedweller Studio
Illustration: Will Hobbs

Color Reproduction by Dot Gradations Ltd, UK
Printed and bound in China by South China Printing Company

12 11 10 09 08
10 9 8 7 6 5 4 3 2 1

New edition ISBNs: 978 1 4329 1237 6 (hardcover)
                    978 1 4329 1248 2 (paperback)

The Library of Congress has cataloged the first edition as follows:
Anderson, Catherine, 1974-
    Daddylonglegs / Catherine Anderson.
        p. cm. — (Bug books)
    Summary: Describes the physical characteristics, habits, and natural environment of the tall spiderlike daddylonglegs.
    Includes bibliographical references (p.   ).
    ISBN: 1-40340-763-0 (HC), 1-40340-994-3 (Pbk.)
    1. Opiliones- - Juvenile literature. [1. Daddy longlegs.] I. Title. II. Series.
    QL458.5 .A53 2003
    595.4'3- -dc21
                                    2002004361

Acknowledgments
The publishers would like to thank the following for permission to reproduce photographs:
© Ann & Rob Simpson p. 21; © Bryan E. Reynolds p. 25; © Corbis pp. 17 (Michael & Patricia Fogden), 23 (Michael T. Sedam); © FLPA (Jeremy Early) p. 18; © Getty Images (Photodisc) p. 20; © James C. Cokendolpher pp. 7 **(left)**, 9, 26; © James H. Robinson p. 7 (right); © James P. Rowan p. 5; © JLM Visuals (Richard P. Jacobs) p. 16; © John S. Reid p. 10; © NHPA (Haroldo Palo Jr.) p. 22; © Oxford Scientific Films pp. 6 (David Fox), 11 (Marshall Black); © Photo Researchers Inc. pp. 15 (Stephen Dalton), 28 (Stephen P. Parker), 29 (Gary Retherford); © Scott Braut pp. 19, 24; © Stuart Wilson p. 8; © Visuals Unlimited pp. 4 (Jonathan D. Speer), 12 (Mary Cummins), 13 (Bill Beatty); © William E. Ferguson pp. 14, 27.

Cover photograph of a daddy longlegs walking across a leaf reproduced with permission of Getty Images (National Geographic/Brian G. Green).

The publishers would like to thank Dr. William Shear, Department of Biology, Hampden-Sydney College, for his assistance in the preparation of the first edition of this book.

Contents

Some words are shown in bold, **like this**. You can find out what they mean by looking in the glossary.

What Are Daddy Longlegs?

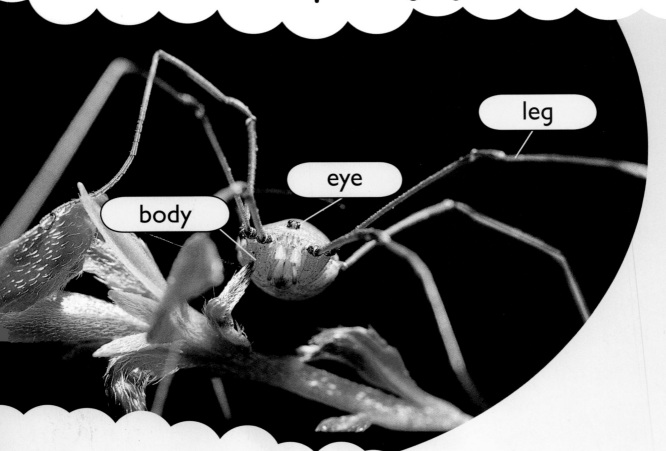

body

eye

leg

A daddy longlegs has a round body and eight very skinny legs. The legs are covered with short hairs. A daddy longlegs has two eyes on the top of its body.

Daddy longlegs are **arachnids**.
They are related to **spiders**. But
they are not real spiders. They do
not make **webs**.

5

Some people call this **spider** a daddy longlegs. But it is a cellar spider. It is a real spider. It spins a **web**.

You can see two body parts on a real spider. A daddy longlegs' body parts are joined together in one piece.

spider

daddy longlegs

How Big Are Daddy Longlegs?

A daddy longlegs can bend its long legs in many places. Some have front legs as long as your hand.

The body of a daddy longlegs is usually the size of your smallest fingernail. But it can be as big as a grape! **Male** daddy longlegs are smaller than **females**.

How Are Daddy Longlegs Born?

female

egg

Daddy longlegs **mate** in the fall. The **female** lays 20 to 30 tiny eggs. She lays them in wet ground. The eggs stay in the ground through the winter.

The eggs **hatch** in the spring.
Baby daddy longlegs look like their
parents. They are very tiny. Each one
is smaller than the period at the end
of this sentence.

How Do Daddy Longlegs Grow?

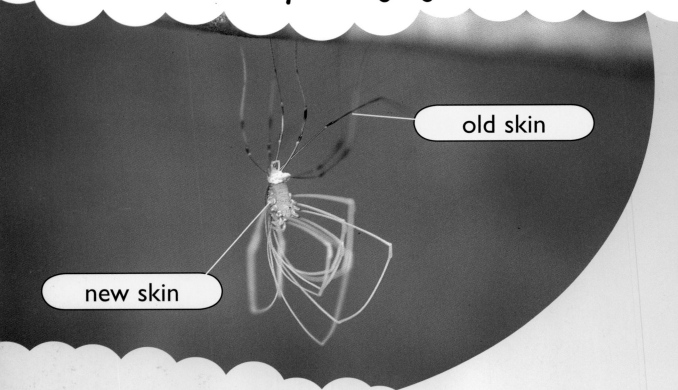

old skin

new skin

As a baby daddy longlegs grows, its skin gets too small. The skin splits down the back. The daddy longlegs slowly crawls out of the old skin. There is a new skin underneath. This is called **molting**.

12

Young daddy longlegs molt every 10 days. They grow bigger after each molt. After two to three months, they are adults.

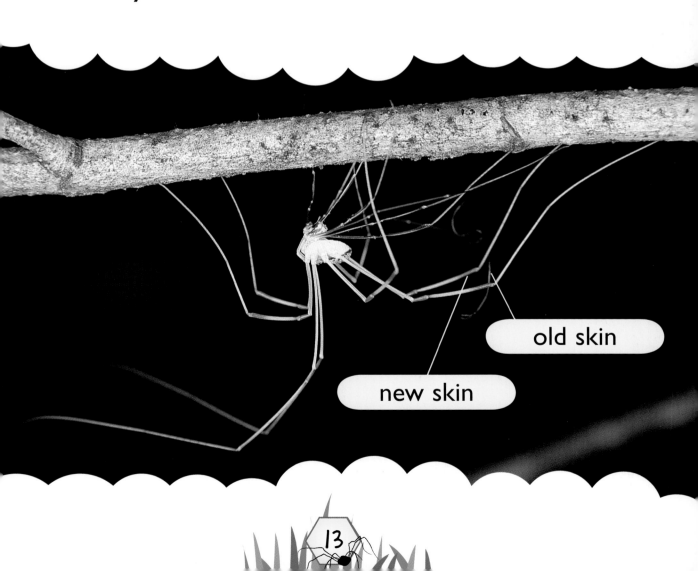

old skin

new skin

How Do Daddy Longlegs Move?

Daddy longlegs move using their eight legs. They can run very fast. They can also climb up walls or trees.

At the end of each leg is a small claw. Daddy longlegs use these claws to hold on to things. They can even hang upside-down.

What Do Daddy Longlegs Eat?

Some daddy longlegs eat fruit and flowers. Others are **predators**. They eat small insects, snails, and worms. Some daddy longlegs are **scavengers**. They eat dead animals.

16

Daddy longlegs have mouthparts that work like small scissors. They break the food into tiny pieces.

Which Animals Attack Daddy Longlegs?

parasite

Sometimes red **parasites** live on daddy longlegs. They can hurt them. Birds, ants, and **spiders** all eat daddy longlegs.

18

The legs of a daddy longlegs come off easily. If a **predator** pulls off a leg it will keep wiggling. The predator watches the leg while the daddy longlegs runs away.

Where Do Daddy Longlegs Live?

Daddy longlegs live all over the world. They live under logs and rocks and on tree trunks. Most live in warm, wet places. Some live in the desert.

In some places, daddy longlegs live in a group. They all wiggle when a **predator** is near. This may scare the predator away.

How Long Do Daddy Longlegs Live?

Daddy longlegs live for about one year.
Most types of daddy longlegs die soon
after they **mate**.

Some daddy longlegs are **endangered**. People go into daddy longlegs' **habitats** such as this cave. This disturbs them and they cannot live there anymore.

What Do Daddy Longlegs Do?

Daddy longlegs cannot see well. They use their legs to hear, taste, and smell. Tiny hairs on their legs help them feel things. Daddy longlegs **preen** their legs to keep them clean.

Daddy longlegs do not have **fangs** or **venom**. They cannot hurt other animals by biting. But some daddy longlegs use the spines on their legs to pinch.

spine

How are Daddy Longlegs Special?

If a **predator** pulls a leg off a daddy longlegs, it will still live. A daddy longlegs cannot grow a new leg, but it can live without one or two.

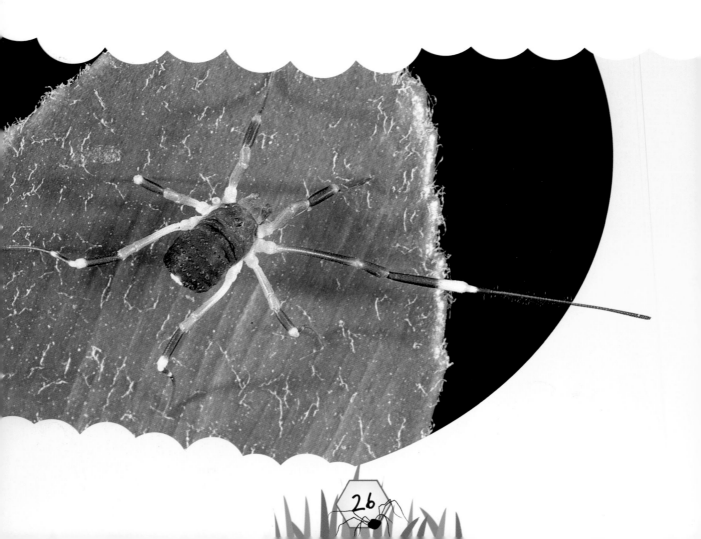

26

Many daddy longlegs make a smelly liquid to **protect** themselves. The liquid can burn a **predator's** mouth and eyes.

Thinking About Daddy Longlegs

How many body parts does this daddy longlegs have? How many does a real **spider** have?

28

Why do these daddy longlegs live in a group? Why might it help them to stay safe?

Bug Map

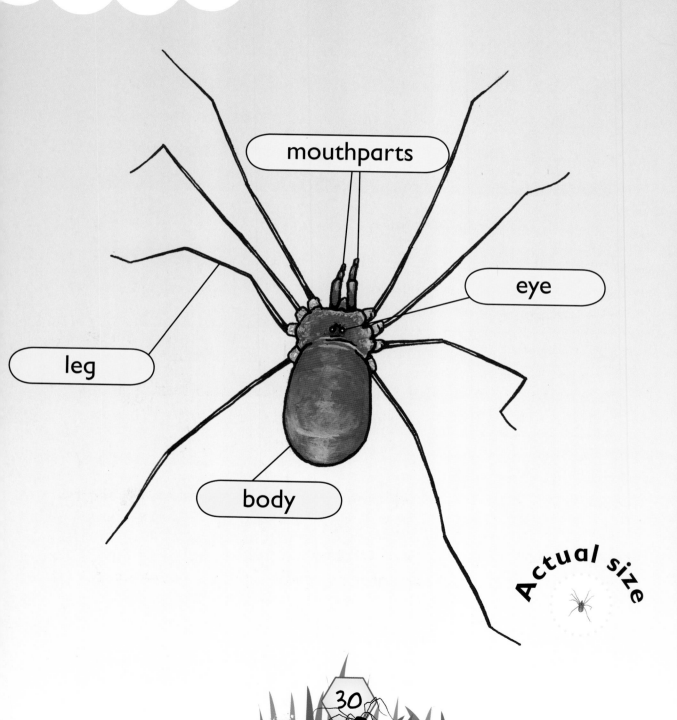

mouthparts

eye

leg

body

Actual size

Glossary

arachnids group of animals that includes spiders, ticks, and scorpions

endangered at risk of dying out forever

fang special mouthpart shaped like a claw. It has a tube inside for venom to come out.

habitat place where an animal lives

hatch break out of an egg

female animal that can lay eggs or give birth to live young

male animal that can mate with a female to produce young

mate when a male and female animal come together to produce young

molting time in an insect's life when it gets too big for its skin. The old skin drops off and a new skin is underneath.

parasite animal that lives on another animal and harms it

predator animal that hunts and eats other animals

preen clean. Animals preen their fur, feathers, or skin.

protect keep safe

scavenger animal that finds and eats food that is already dead

spider animal with eight legs that can make silk

venom liquid that can harm an animal

web net made from sticky threads of silk. Spiders use webs to catch food.

Index

More Books to Read

Claybourne, Anna. *Beetles, Bugs and Pests*. London: Hodder Children's Division, 2003.

Hughes, Monica. *Spiders*. Chicago: Heinemann Library, 2004.

Swanson, Diane. *Bugs Up Close*. Toronto, ON: Kids Can Press, Ltd, 2007.

32